# Homesteading

*A Comprehensive Homestead Guide to Self-Sufficiency, Raising Backyard Chickens, and Mini Farming, Including Gardening Tips and Best Practices for Growing Your Own Food*

# Contents

# Introduction

What do Academy Award winners Nicole Kidman, Julia Roberts, Reese Witherspoon, and Russell Crowe, alongside *Friends* star Jennifer Aniston and actress Vera Farmiga have in common?

Apart from living life as Hollywood A-listers, these people are also famous for embracing the life of a homesteader. But what is so hot about homesteading that even the red-carpet walkers are drawn to it?

It is ironic that no matter how successful people tend to become and how many different places they go in life, their primal instinct kicks in, somehow, and they always go back to Mother Nature and her bounties. Homesteading has become a catharsis for people who finally want to live the life of a producer rather than a mere consumer.

And if you have been mulling over the idea of raising chickens, goats, pigs, and cattle while also tending a vegetable and fruit garden, then you are not alone. Thousands of people all over the globe have decided to say "yes" to gardening and domesticating animals – and why wouldn't they?

There is so much more to homesteading than just producing your own stocks of milk, eggs, meat, veggies, and even crafting your own soaps and candles. It is also not just putting a parcel of land to good use.

If you are growing tired of a complex lifestyle and just want to live a fuss-free life, then homesteading is for you. It means embracing wholesome values that have been forgotten by many.

Do you want to leave better memories for your children? Then homesteading allows them to conquer themselves – and not just the levels in a video game. If you are stubbornly independent and want to be self-sufficient, then the life of a homesteader is the best way of existence for you.

Homesteading simply makes sense, doesn't it? But, of course, freedom brings with it a plethora of responsibilities – and this is your Day One. Some skills need to be learned (and even unlearned), there are laws to be mindful of, and even many challenges ahead.

The beauty of homesteading, though, is that you change your life for the better – forever. If everyone in your family is ready to dive in, then this is it! Prepare to learn the foundational knowledge and skills that will make you an expert homesteader in no time.

Welcome to your newest adventure.

# PART ONE: HOMESTEADING BASICS

# Homesteading Explained

Once upon a time, President Abraham Lincoln made available acres upon acres of land to adults who never took arms against the U.S. federal government, women, and immigrants. The Homestead Act of 1862 offered land ownership to these peoples to address the inequalities that were quite rampant back then.

This Act is considered one of the most important legislative acts in American history because public domains - approximately 270 million acres or about ten percent of the United States area - were given to private citizens. Settlers just needed to build a home on their parcel of land, make improvements, and then farm the land for five years so they would be deemed eligible for proving up or becoming the legal owner.

If you look at it, at one point in history, everyone practiced homesteading, where physical labor was the norm. Fast-forward to modern times, and it has turned into a much wider spectrum.

Many people talk about homesteading. Yet when asked to define what it means, there are varied answers. Some say that it means you can provide your own solar, water, or wind-powered electric generators. Some claim that pure homesteading means bartering over the use of money. Still, some define homesteading as letting go of lucrative careers and signing up for a more simplistic way of living.

But how would you define homesteading?

The broadest meaning of this term is being able to commit to a life of self-sufficiency. This could encompass growing as well as preserving your own food, making fabrics for your own clothing and, yes, even providing electricity through natural means.

As you learn more about homesteading, you will realize that not all homesteaders share the same set of values. In fact, it is a diverse bunch of people who say "yes" to this way of life. You will find that there are people who homestead because they are just tired of the daily grind of urban living. Some want to prepare for economic hardships. Still, others just enjoy tilling the land and watching things grow as they plant, harvest, and then preserve their own foods.

Whatever your reasons for considering homesteading or learning more about it, one thing is certain - you have just made a noble decision.

First off, homesteading is a humbling experience, an eye-opener as to how finite life can be and how small you are in contrast to the universe (or multiverse as other people would believe).

Some crops grow and are harvested, while others simply fail. Even the best of farming plans can fail, and so saying "yes" to this way of life is an attempt to tame a piece of Mother Earth and wait for her blessings to come. And as the successes and failures of nature humble you, you also learn to persevere and pray because you have finally comprehended that life is not always within your control.

Homesteading also teaches strength. Talk to older people - especially the ones who grew up on a farm - and they will tell you that they learned to milk cows when they were barely school age. Young girls also cooked side by side with their mothers - all are environments that are now unfamiliar to today's generation.

Kids, back in the day, were capable of thriving even in the harshest circumstances, and this is the very thing that the world badly needs. Homesteading builds the strongest work ethics so that even the youngest children in your family will know how to contribute in terms of labor.

A homestead is one of the greatest places to raise your children. Living in this farm-like setting is schooling in itself. Kids who are trained in these settings can see, hear, and understand more. They will grow up to be more responsible because they are the ones who will think twice before wasting food or polluting their environment.

Talk of growing things and producing your own food, yet another reason for homesteading is the want for food to taste better. You have probably eaten in a restaurant somewhere and complained about the flat-tasting meat or bland salad.

Eggs and meat taste best when fresh, and so do tomatoes and other produce.

The great news is that you do not have to suffer through another flavorless meal anymore. You can now take the conscious effort to live self-sufficiently and enjoy the foods in the process. But to be able to enjoy that fresh tomato, be ready to put in months of hard work as you plant the seeds, make sure that the seedlings grow, and then plan the correct time to plant them in the ground.

And even then, you are not done yet because you need to protect the tomato plant against the harsh weather, set up a trellis for them, and then wait for the right moment when they have ripened.

At the end of the day, you will also realize that homesteading instills appreciation in you because nothing better teaches about this than hard work. You will also have a renewed sense of value for growing your own nutritious food. Moreover, the amount of energy that you need to exert just to raise chickens, pigs, or cattle is astonishing. Add to this the thought of butchering the animal that you raised, and the work becomes doubly difficult.

No matter how difficult, though, all these add to your knowledge of Mother Nature and how learning about gardening, breeding animals, bee farming, pollination, making cheese, and such, could lead to true freedom and independence.

Now, don't think that you are going to be like your great-grandparents who had to plow the land by hand (though this is your choice, too). The great thing about the 21st century is that you have access to farming equipment, better health care, and the means of staying connected to the world (some homesteaders blog and keep Instagram accounts so they can inspire others). All these can be used for and not against your chosen lifestyle as a homesteader.

Homesteading is also far from an easy life because you need to commit to physical, emotional, and mental labor to make this lifestyle a success. Oddly, even when it requires these different human aspects, it guarantees that you will live a stress-free life.

So how does homesteading equate to zero stress if manual labor is involved? The answer is in the amount of security and peace that is often linked to self-sufficiency and so, in turn, to homesteading. These days, people have the chance to live a healthier lifestyle when they choose to live in home-based farms or even when they simply decide to grow an indoor garden.

Many homesteaders have reported that living on a farm or in the country is much more relaxing than setting up home in a city. They also feel freer and healthier in such an environment. They can even save money on clothing and food. Some even make money through trading and selling the goods that they produce in their homes.

And who could argue the wellness that comes with the great outdoors? Even young kids can learn about their connection to nature. City life only provides parks, but homesteading offers much more. It offers respite from the serious threats of genetically modified crops and foods.

So, what is this big fuss over genetically modified foods?

It has been 27 years since the first genetically modified food was introduced onto the market, and the American diet has since consumed huge amounts of this manipulated foodstuff. It is not surprising that genetically modified organisms (GMOs) or genetically engineered (GE) products now dominate many agribusiness sectors. It is likewise alarming that biotech and chemical companies now control seed suppliers.

You are eating these dangerous foods if you are not buying organic or not growing your own food in your backyard. Just think about the modified crops that are now in many grocery shops – corns, rapeseed (used in making canola oil), peppers, zucchini, squash, sugar cane, rice, papaya, and peas – and you would be distressed about where to get your next nutritious meal.

The GMO producers are literally out of control, insomuch that the small print will not even indicate that the corn and soy that you bought are GMOs. Prevention Magazine cited that 80 percent of processed foods are genetically modified – and that is a lot. So, it matters that you check if your food has a non-GMO label. What is even better is if you grow your food, that way, you are guaranteed that no pesticides were used.

Choosing to become a homesteader, therefore, becomes much more promising because more people are joining the bandwagon. In a world of genetic engineering and GMO companies winning court battles against farmers, the good news is that homesteading is now a global social cause.

This is the perfect moment to turn into a homesteader and not worry about the high expenses brought about by living in the city. And as the job market is becoming more erratic, there is the logic in considering country living and joining many others who now enjoy healthier, more peaceful lives.

Modern homesteading offers more possibilities and choices nowadays, so roll up those sleeves because it is time to sing heigh-ho.

# What Type of Homesteader Are You?

Now that you know the benefits that come with homesteading, it is time to find out what kind of homesteader you are. If Dictionary.com defines the term as any dwelling with its land and buildings where a family makes its home, then the act becomes a lot simpler but, nowadays, homesteading goes beyond setting up a structure and letting your family stay there.

Since homesteading is also about being self-sustaining, then it could also mean that it is not just another place where you feel at home; it's also the zone where dreams are built, and wellness is upheld.

Homesteading is the place where the family lives as one and works as one. Sure, it could mean living off-grid for some families or just wanting to save some more money on organic foods, but ultimately, every family needs to set their homesteading goals.

Homesteading could mean many different things, but one of its most important goals is self-sustenance or being less dependent upon others. There are also five different kinds of homesteaders, and it is time to find out which of these you are.

# The Urban/Apartment Homesteader

One of the greatest things about modern homesteading is its flexibility. Gone are the days when homesteading is thought of as a thing for ranchers and farmers only. There is no need to own thousands of acres of land anymore just to be called a homesteader. These definitions are quickly changing so, no matter where you are, you can now be a homesteader.

If you are currently living in the suburbia, specifically in an apartment, no worries, you still have unlimited possibilities in terms of starting your homestead.

But what would homesteading look like inside a tiny apartment? How about in a small backyard?

Living in a city should not limit your homesteading dreams. You could live in the heart of the city jungle and have breakfast on a tiny balcony each morning but could still live the life of a homesteader.

### Characteristics that Define the Best Apartment Homesteaders

• The dwelling unit is small. Homegrown fruits and vegetables are your keys to sustainable living, but where there's limited space, these plants have no room to grow, so if you've been wracking your brain on where to put your vegetable pots, then you're definitely an urban homesteader. The urban homestead is also characterized by single-family habitats.

• The household size is about three persons. A report prepared by the United States Department of Housing and Urban Development Office of Policy Development and Research showed that the mean number of persons in an urban homestead is at three point two.

• A newly formed household. The same study also proved that about 15 percent of the urban homesteaders said they were not heads of their previous households.

• Previously lived in rental properties. The statistics show that 90 percent of urban homesteaders were previously renters.

• Full-time or part-time employees. It's also been found that 90 percent of urban homesteaders were working full time or part time before becoming homesteaders.

• Modest savings. One of the probable reasons why urban dwellers also want to become homesteaders is the chance to augment their incomes through gardening or keeping livestock.

• Optimized use of space. First, you can grow different herbs in small pots, but you have to know the right spot to put them. And the best apartment homesteaders use areas such as the windowsill, the balcony, and even nooks and crannies just to grow their veggies and herbs. These are the people who enjoy tending onions, oregano, garlic, and herbs in smaller containers. If you're okay with such a setup, then you probably live in a tiny apartment at the moment. If the idea of a hydroponic garden is not just exciting to you but also a solution to your gardening issues, then you're definitely an apartment homesteader. Likewise if the idea of visiting local farmers at local farms excites you. When you're free, and your idea of "me time" is to visit the farmers' market to buy fresh milk and eggs, then it's possible you don't currently enjoy them because you're living in the city – specifically, in a small space.

• You want to begin a homestead pantry for your family. So what are the skills that city-dwellers turning into homesteaders often have? Small-scale fermenting, canning, seed saving, knitting, sewing, water management, rooftop beekeeping, and even soap and candle making are skills that were common to your grandparents. But these are now common urban homesteading skills, too.

If you are also in search of neighborhood elders who can teach you the skills or attend lectures and classes in your local area, then you're a true-blue urban homesteader. This is also true if your source of knowledge is the city library.

If you have been secretly wishing to learn food preservation so you can preserve your bulk food purchases, then you are ready to become an urban homesteader to provide food for your family.

On a personal level, if you prefer wearing barefoot sandals while going around and spraying the organic anti-bug mixture on your potted plants, or if your idea of a pet is having a cat, a toy dog, and a cute turtle, then these just prove that you are an urban-dweller.

Don't worry, though, because even if your idea of a vacation is to visit city museums, you could still start homesteading. It is all a matter of learning the right skills meant for such settings.

## The Medium to Large-Scale Homesteaders

What makes bigger scale homesteading different are aspects such as fruit trees, a berry patch or two, a vegetable garden, bigger composting, rain barrels, livestock, and bigger parcels of land in contrast to the limited spaces in the city.

The land size also indicates whether you are a small, medium, or large-scale homesteader. The measurements are:

Small homestead – six to ten acres of land.

Medium homestead – 11 to 30 acres

Large homestead – 75 to 200 acres

Apart from the acreage, here are the telltale signs that define larger land homesteaders:

• Hard work is your everyday reality. Your idea of a workout is hiking, kayaking, lifting heavy objects, or taking long walks around your neighborhood.

And if you don't even need a cup of coffee to jump-start your morning, then you're probably already used to routine, morning physical work and are, therefore, meant for larger-scale homesteading.

• You dream of rows upon rows of different plants. If you can't picture yourself tending to mere pots and containers, then you're definitely cut out for large-scale homesteading.

• You are thinking of expanding the workforce. One of the most obvious signs that you're about to live in a large homestead is when you're already thinking of employing more people to help you with your homesteading operation. If your family members are no longer enough to cover all of the tasks on your homestead, then you know you've got a larger piece of land.

• You're also thinking of bigger investments. Bigger workforce, livestock, and gardening all require additional money or investment. Most of the time, the glaring large-scale homesteaders add bigger machinery and equipment so that the work on the homestead is made lighter.

### Machinery That is Often Added

o Tractor (costs north of $10,000)

o An all-terrain vehicle (small ATVs can cost as little as $1,000 while the biggest ones could cost as much as a tractor)

o Farm truck

o Wagon

o Backhoe

o Cultivator

o Plows

o Harrows

o Balers

o Harvester

• You think you need an irrigation system. You know that you're a medium to large-scale homesteader if you've been planning to set up an irrigation system to water your garden.

• You want to share your produce with your neighbors. If you desire to grow food beyond what you can store in your family's homestead pantry, then you're ready for a large-scale homestead. You are more than a hobby farmer at this point; you're already thinking of blessing lives outside that of your home.

So, have you figured out what kind of a homesteader you are? Now it is time to answer a simple "yes" or "no" to a series of questions:

1. Do you often worry where your food originates?

2. Do you wish to become self-reliant?

3. Do you like cooking your own food, or are you willing to learn?

4. Are you okay with learning traditional skills, such as carpentry, sewing, knitting, candle making, doing your own laundry, and others?

5. Would you be willing to learn skills so you can protect your family during an emergency?

6. Could you butcher animals for organic meat?

7. Would you consider the thought of raising animals for your sustenance?

8. In your opinion, is living off-grid an appealing way to live?

9. Are planting and food preservation exciting things to do on your own or with your family?

10. Would you be able to live miles away from the grocery store?

If you answered "yes" to most or all of these questions, then you are absolutely ready to wear those farming boots.

# Steps Before You Start Homesteading

Congratulations! At this point, you have bravely said "yes" to becoming a homesteader. Now your sleeves are rolled up, and you are ready for the tasks, so what is next?

Your next step is to prepare mentally and physically for the days and years of hard work ahead. This phase is the key to staying and not giving up once the challenges appear.

Planning for homesteading is not all about knowing what to feed the chickens or how many gallons of milk can be squeezed from one cow. Before you even buy your first packet of seeds or your farming boots, you need to know some behind-the-scenes stuff so that you won't be caught unaware.

Being in control of your food, health, and home, in general, is commendable.

Here are the crucial steps that every future homesteader needs to take before making the huge leap:

## Commit

Starting a homestead from scratch is a daunting task, so it helps to break the responsibilities down into smaller and easier steps. Decide the things that you want to commit to before you even set foot towards achieving them.

Take the time to research, read, ask the right questions, and take down notes. Be ready for the unexpected by setting up buffers (e.g., knowledge and money).

Another part of your commitment is to alter your mindset. As soon as you are ready, decide to make things rather than readily buy them, or reuse rather than toss them. As you start preferring these, then you are on your way to becoming a homesteader.

Your life is no longer a life of consumerism, so a part of the commitment is also to downsize. A coffee or waffle maker will no longer have use in a homestead. There are many items that you currently own that should go. The things that have been in storage bins and boxes for years are probably not going to be used anyway, so donate them, give them away to friends, sell them, or simply dump them.

## Assess Yourself

Statistics show that there are more introverted homesteaders, and this is easy to understand because the wide-open spaces that typically come with homesteading foster much alone time, fewer neighbors, and room for the kids to run around.

Homesteading is synonymous with adventure once you set out to do it because the clucking chickens, growing vegetables and fruits in the garden, even the pantry that is slowly filling up with preserved food in jars are as exciting as homesteading could get. But there is a side to this life that could get flat-out melancholic as living in the country potentially leads to isolation.

As soon as the dust begins to settle (so to speak), you might begin to miss the conveniences that are offered in the city – from ready-made meals to the cinema. The walls could feel confining if you have not taken the time to assess yourself before homesteading. If you are an introvert, then you could get energized when you are alone as compared to the extroverts who get their energy by socializing with people (now this second batch will need more help in terms of keeping sadness at bay).

This does not mean that extroverts are not effective homesteaders, though. It is just a reality that a few families have struggled with. Rural loneliness is real, as people have admitted during their homesteading battles, but there is much room for different types of personalities when it comes to the homesteading gig.

Understand what motivates you. Introverts are project-driven so you can focus your energies on the projects that are in front of you. You have probably heard of homesteading mothers who took care of their kids while they also deep-cleaned their house and gardened about but who still felt bored, so think twice if you can take this project head-on.

It also helps to understand that rural living does not mean being cut off from the rest of the world. You can still access social networks so you can join forums where you can share ideas with like-minded people. This could be a great source of social stimulation. Even when these people are just your online friends, still, you get to keep a social discourse and, in the process, maintain your mental balance.

Assess now if you can keep yourself occupied and not be dragged down by the so-called cabin fever (irritability and restlessness as a reaction to claustrophobia). Homesteading requires a 180-degree turn from an easy life, so face the mirror and be honest with your answer as you ask yourself: Are you truly ready to become a homesteader?

If the thought of being self-sufficient and knowing where your food comes from weighs more than any difficulties ahead, then go ahead and sign up to a life of homemade ice creams and homegrown meats.

## Find New Friends

You can socialize online, or you can do it the old-fashioned way as you find homesteaders like you (preferably your neighbors) and befriend them. You will even have more people to barter with for your future produce and livestock.

And those homesteading questions? You can finally put them to rest if you ask your new homesteading friends about their experiences of homesteading laws, weather, general climate, etc.

Having friends also means having someone to borrow things from during emergencies. You can borrow a dehydrator from a new friend in exchange for your canner.

## Plan

There is a saying that if you fail to plan, then you plan to fail. As with anything, planning involves setting realistic goals.

Many people feel overwhelmed when they start homesteading. This is understandable, but it can be managed when you set goals that you can reasonably handle. You can set seasonal goals instead of distributing your tasks across different goals. This will just lead to confusion, so tackle your projects one month or one weekend at a time.

You also need to plan on an extra income while you are still establishing your homestead. It is okay to dream that homesteading can provide all of your needs, but this is not realistic.

You need to seriously consider the expenses that come with setting up your self-sustaining habitat. Also, you might be used to eating out or traveling, so you need to find out how much of this you are willing to give up.

What is great about modern homesteading is that your lifestyle choices have greatly widened, as more income opportunities are now available to you. As opposed to your forebearers, you now have access to more information, so you are less likely to commit the greenhorn homesteader mistakes.

This could include taking on an online job while you are homesteading. Thanks to the Internet, there are now more job opportunities, even in remote areas.

An online business is also not that expensive to set up. Selling wood cookstoves over the Internet might not be a lucrative source of income, but it can still provide a few thousand dollars annually, enough to cover some of the homesteading expenses.

### Write Down Your Plan

You can also brainstorm as a family regarding the homestead layout. A graphing notebook is your best friend as you sketch the floor plans to scale. Fill the pages with storage space, the pantry, and other functional spaces.

However, the layout is not the biggest concern in terms of planning for homesteading – financial preparation is. But don't worry – there are basic money principles that can help you cope.

First, say "no" to debt. Starting your homesteading project using borrowed money is not a good idea. This goes against every homesteading principle, more specifically, self-sufficiency.

Homesteaders generally want to detach from money issues. An experienced homesteader prefers bartering rather than buying anything. Many just leave a single credit card for emergency purposes.

Homesteading also means being prepared for emergencies, such as equipment damages, injuries, illness, and such. Be sure to set aside an emergency fund.

Keeping up with the Joneses is not the way to live your homesteading life, especially when you want to avoid bankruptcy like the plague. Just stop comparing yourself with other Pinterest, picture-perfect homesteading families. Remember that what you see on people's social accounts is just the façade and not the real picture, so just water the grass from your side of the lawn, and you will be awed at how your mindset improves.

Financial preparation also means being aware of money pits, especially when your budget is tight. You will soon grasp that generating your own food is pricier than buying it at the store, and it is much easier to purchase a gallon of milk than to keep a cow for milk. However, homesteading is now your way of life; it is raising kids who appreciate Mother Nature, the value of hard work, and many other things. So, yes, homesteading – at least some aspects of it – is going to cost more.

Have an abundance mindset – you need one if you want to transition from an easy life to homesteading successfully. With this kind of mindset, you will feel more at peace about time management, resource management, and even your finances.

### Embrace Minimalism

While you are encouraged to have a positive mental outlook, this does not mean keeping a garish lifestyle. It can be so easy to get caught up with the thought that you always need to acquire more or do more in life, but doing only the things that matter is the best way to go.

If there is anything in your life – anything at all – that has been draining your energy, time, and money that you can finally eliminate, then now is the time to let it go.

If your kids have signed up for a lot of activities at school or if you have had to drag yourself to an event like book club, then you just have to say "no." Even if these things are good, if they don't make you truly happy, then there is no point in adding them to your calendar.

### Look at Challenges as a Way to Foster Growth

Homesteading is a way of life that can be demanding, but it can also be fun and rewarding. Setting your mind to this will help you through the roughest patches. Understand that every setback and mistake will provide a learning experience.

And don't forget to ask any farmer to tell you about his or her past errors and you will surely be told that those mistakes also helped stage their eventual success.

Find out if homesteading is right for you. If you like providing for you and your family's needs, and putting in hours of physical labor won't deter you, then homesteading is something that you will surely enjoy.

# 11 Essential Homesteading Skills

Okay, homesteading means survival; you get that now. Yet even the most efficient carpenter, welder, and truck driver can have the skills that will work fantastically on a homestead, but, individually, they might not survive. You need to have an information arsenal that will cover topics that are needed in sustaining your new chosen lifestyle.

However, you do not have to become an expert gardener on your first day. Knowing how to plant and cultivate are skills that could help you, though. Having a passion for them will even contribute to a livelier garden.

You can start small when it comes to your skills, and today that is what you are going to do. Begin small by taking the time to know which homesteading skills you need to tackle first.

## Composting

Every time you repurpose products or reduce waste on your homestead is a win-win situation for you. Remember that composting is the skill that conquers both.

The compost area is not difficult to set up whether you are working on a small piece of land or a bigger one. You can take the easier route by using a trash bin as your initial compost area or install a more complex compost area using palettes or plywood.

Composting skills can be as basic as gathering grass clippings, straw, natural food waste, and other organic materials, at first. When this pile of waste decomposes, then you already have a compost soil that can be used as a garden fertilizer.

## Gardening

Are you planting the correct kinds of crops for the climate in your area? Are you also providing ample space for the root vegetables to grow? Will you be able to distinguish and prevent crop diseases?

Study the crops that you will plant and then strategize your planting methods. Till the ground, use the windowsills, hang pots, create a fence of edible plants, and use just about every possible piece of the landscape on your homestead to maximize the use of your land. If you live in an apartment, make the most of every available space.

Study which plants grow in what parts and which ones can grow side by side.

In a nutshell, your gardening skills should include knowing:

• When to plant.

• The distance between planted seeds.

• What requires propagating.

• What should be included in a greenhouse.

• What pot sizes to use.

• Germination and maturation periods.

• What pests will ravage your crops.

• What vegetables work together.

• When to harvest your crops.

## Salvaging

Your fruits and vegetables are all great sustainable sources of organic food. So, the next skill that you need to learn is how to save the seeds that you can replant properly. Bell peppers, cherry tomatoes, carrots, and blueberries can be replanted. All you need are a sharp knife and pruning shears to harvest the seeds and then store.

Using the pruning shears, cut off the seed pods. Place the pods in a room with a warm temperature. This has to be a low-humidity room. Spread these on newspaper or several pieces of paper towels.

Let dry for one-two weeks.

## Food Storage

Any city dweller can always run to the local grocery store to buy pasta, flour, and canned goods, but these will not provide you with a balanced diet. You still need fruits, protein sources, and vegetables to obtain essential vitamins and minerals – and what better way to flood your system with these essentials than to eat organic?

There are many forms of food storage, and you will have to learn these to live on your homestead effectively. You can do any of these inexpensively using techniques such as canning, drying, and freezing.

Canning is the application of heat to food that has been sealed in jars. This process destroys microorganisms that lead to spoilage. The right canning techniques prevent spoilage by food heating for a specified time and driving out air from the jars, thus, creating a vacuum seal.

The United States of Agriculture (USDA) approves only two canning methods: pressure canning and water-bath canning.

Pressure canning uses a big kettle producing steam inside a sealed compartment. The packed jars that are in the kettle need to reach an internal temperature of 240 degrees. A dial gauge is then used to measure the amount of pressure that the jars go through.

Pressure canning is best used in processing meat, fish, poultry, and vegetables.

Water-bath canning, on the other hand, is the method that is also called hot water canning. It also uses a big kettle with boiling water. The difference is that the filled jars are placed underwater and then heated up to 212 degrees for some time. This method is best used for foods that have a high acidity level, such as fruits, tomatoes, and pickled foods.

Of all the food preservation methods, drying is the oldest. A portion of the food that is being dried is exposed to high temperatures so that moisture is removed but only to a point where it will not cook. Air circulation is a factor in evenly dried food.

There are now electric dehydrators complete with a fan and a thermostat that help regulate the temperature for food drying. The oven can also be used, or the heat of the sun, but these latter processes take longer, and the results are far inferior compared to those that were dried inside a dehydrator.

Food freezing is a process of preparing, packing, and subjecting foods to freezing temperatures while they are still fresh. Fruits, vegetables, fish, meats, cakes, pieces of bread, casseroles, and soups can all be frozen.

To freeze food, be sure to wrap food tightly and to keep the freezer door closed at all times. Plan the foods that you will freeze so that the unit will maintain its ideal air circulation.

These processes, along with other food preservation methods, such as fermentation, alcohol immersion, pickling, immersion in olive oil, and preserving in sugar and salt, are time-tested survival skills that your predecessors learned and effectively applied.

### Milling

Depending on where you chose to homestead, storage concerns for larger quantities of grains and flours could pose a challenge. You can still grind a few pounds of grains at a time and then have it stored for baking and cooking purposes.

The simplest modern way to mill flour is to use a food processor. Feed ten cups of flour into the hopper; then, you will get ultra-fine flour in a few minutes. If you want to do it naturally, then you can use the good old-fashioned mortar and pestle. You can also buy a mixer attachment specially made for milling grains or a portable grain mill.

## Butter and Cheese Making

There is no need to own a cow just to make your first homemade butter. What you need is just a bit of cream and a jar that you can shake it in. As for cheeses, you can also make ricotta cheese, mascarpone, Chèvre, and maple yogurt cheese.

Cheeses can be made from any kind of milk, including sheep, goat, and cow. The kind of coagulant used depends on the kind of cheese that you want to make. Acid cheeses need an acid source like acetic acid (vinegar acid) or a glucono delta-lactone or mild food acid.

### Method:

1. Begin with fresh, warm milk. The fresher the milk, the more scrumptious the cheese.

2. Acidify the milk using citric acid. A liter of milk should be mixed with three point five grams of acid.

3. Add a coagulant (rennet).

4. Using your clean hand, press the surface of the milk to test the firmness of the formed gel.

5. Using a cheese harp, whisk or knife, cut the formed curds. Keep in mind that the smaller the slices, the drier they will be. Cut bigger pieces, and you'll have a moister cheese.

6. Turn on the stove, then continuously stir while cooking the curds.

7. Wash the curds (whey removal) by taking some of the whey off the vat and then having it replaced with water.

8. Drain by using a colander. You could also wait ten minutes so that the curds will finally settle to the bottom.

9. Press the curds at the bottom while they are still hot.

10. Salt and age.

## Animal Husbandry

The most efficient homesteaders are those who depend on animals. They are those who have horses to ride, dogs that guard, chickens that provide meat and eggs, and pigs that eventually become bacon and ham.

The Encyclopedia Britannica Online defines animal husbandry as controlled cultivation, management, and production of domestic animals, including the improvement of the qualities considered desirable by humans.

Animal husbandry is also associated with beekeeping, dairy farming, and breeding – you will learn more about this later.

## Starting Fire

The cavemen have done it so you can do it, too. As a survivalist, building a fire should already be second nature to you. The drill is this:

1. First, create a tinder nest. This is where the starter flame will be sparked.

2. Next, make the notch and place bark under it. Begin spinning, then build your fire. Prepare the fireboard and then keep rubbing.

3. Start the fire.

If you feel like taking an easier route, then use a magnifying lens to start the fire. Just put the tinder underneath the lens and wait for the beam of the sun to produce a flame.

You will need this skill to cook your food when there's no electricity. The classic bonfire will not just provide warmth but also a place where you can cook your food.

You can also still rely on propane tanks paired with a reliable gas stove. You can also just grill your food to make even more scrumptious meals.

## Cooking

Just as important as growing your own food is learning how to cook healthy meals. If you have been relying on restaurant meals, don't fret, because this skill can be learned.

It is crucial to shop for your own cooking utensils. The essentials are wooden spoons, stirring spoons, spatulas, measuring cups, and a whisk. You should also invest in pots and pans (copper would be a nice material for these). Use cast iron as much as you can as it makes any food taste better, plus it is a durable cooking tool that you can use for many years.

One good paring knife should be enough to begin your cooking lessons.

Purchase cookbooks that were written for beginners. Take the time to read the reviews about each cookbook. If you do not have tangible copies of cookbooks, then you can search for phone apps.

## DIY Natural Remedy and First Aid

Homesteading almost always equates to living miles away from the nearest pharmacy or hospital, so you need to be prepared for self-healing. Concoct homeopathic remedies for minor conditions.

Find herbs and spices in your garden that can be turned into remedies for common ailments. You can make homemade soaps, lotions, and salves. You can also harvest raw honey that is known for treating skin rashes, colds, coughs, burns, and many more ailments.

Another useful set of skills is tending to cuts, burns, and scrapes to prevent infection. Keep a stock of medicine suture accessories, and even a military-grade tourniquet.

Learn also the Heimlich maneuver as well as CPR. Remember, though, that the person still needs medical help after the performance of either First Aid. To do the Heimlich maneuver, do the following:

1. Get behind the person.

2. Lean him or her forward and then give five back blows using the heel of your hand.

3. Put your arms around the choking person's waist.

4. Make a fist, then put it above the navel with your thumb in.

5. Wrap the fist with your other hand, then push upward and inward.

6. Do five abdominal thrusts.

7. Repeat until the person can expel the lodged food or cough on their own.

## As for CPR

1. Put the person on a steady surface.

2. Check the insides of his or her mouth, then tilt their head and chin.

3. Do 100-120 chest compressions every minute.

4. Add two rescue breaths for every 30 chest compressions.

5. Do this until medical help arrives.

## Fortification

You also need to fortify your homestead against robbers and intruders. The ever-reliable security cameras, motion sensors, and traditional alarms play a huge role in keeping your family safe and secure.

There are several options for fencing, including:

- Post and board fence (often seen around horse pastures)

- Split-rail fence

- Electric fence

- Woven wire fence

A woven fence is a good way to secure your homestead because this is a sturdy boundary. You can even top this with barbed wire to make it even more secure.

Your farm dogs can also become your guard dogs. They are one of the best deterrents against robbers.

There are many other homesteading skills that you can add to this list so that you can make your homesteading adventure even more exciting.

# How Much Does Homesteading Cost?

The first time that you delve into it, homesteading can seem simple and quaint. After all, what can be more idyllic than canning your foods, your kids playing with farm animals, or everyone frolicking under the sun, right?

However, as soon as you stake the first post of your fence, you will realize that homesteading can be pricey - especially when you are living off of a single income. Yes, remodeling the house, improving the land, putting up outbuildings, and growing animal herds all cost money.

There are two ways this could go - starting small or going full blast the first time. Say you want to begin homesteading less than an acre of land, where you will have a little house, a garage for two cars, a studio, greenhouse, chicken enclosure, berry bushes, apple trees, a fire pit, and a compost pile - how much do you think it would cost for the upkeep?

The greenhouse could easily cost $1,500 if it is fancier than the $500 pop-up varieties. Other approximate garden costs are:

- $120 for the sod cutter

- $120/day rental for the Rototiller

- $50 for the garden tools (although these can be borrowed from your friends or family on your first few days of homesteading)

- $20 for the seed starting trays

- $160 for the potting soil

- $28/bag of organic worm fertilizers

- $200 transplants

- $25 for the mulch

- $40 for every apple tree

- $8 for every berry bush

- $1,000 for the fence

- $20 for the chicken wire

- $100 for various seeds

- $20 for monthly watering

You can also construct tomato cages using scrap woods. The approximate amount that you would spend for a 1,300 square-foot garden would be about $3,600 from the outset.

This is just a rough estimate of what you would purchase because you would eventually add other products to your monthly expenses. You can cut down on some of the expenses, such as the worm fertilizes and some of the seeds when you finally learn to make your own fertilizers and salvage the seeds.

Transplants can be cut down to 50 percent or be eradicated from the list.

If you are planning on taking care of chickens, here are the costs involved:

- $12 per chick

- $70 for the brood tub

- $12 for the heat lamp

- $15 for the chick feeder

- $15 for the chick waterer

- $200 for the construction of coop and run

- $26 for the hen feeder

- $32 for the hen waterer

- $50 for the water heater (to be used during winter)

- $240/year for the feed or about $20 per month

- $228 annually for the treats

- $60 a year for the bedding

Keeping six chickens would be about $960 every year with an annual upkeep of $500+ for the feed, treats, and bedding.

Beyond these initial amounts, the reality of homesteading is that you can realize your dreams and live the life of a retiree way before you reach your golden years – and these are priceless.

You do not need huge dollar amounts in your bank or investments just to jump-start your homesteading journey. And now that you are a homesteader think of your investments as not just being in the form of money anymore. Even your time can be invested now. An example is when you begin setting up your garden for your self-sufficiency project.

It will cost money to buy the first seeds and other gardening tools, but a huge portion of your effort will result in stock vegetables and fruits in jars and cans. These can last for weeks – even months – depending on how you ration them.

With these foods and eventually the meats to be provided by the livestock, you can make more investments. You will need to keep challenging yourself if you want to live off, or semi-retire on, your homestead.

There isn't a single correct way to do it, but there are guidelines. At the top of these rules is to leave your comfort zone. Pick a monthly expense and then find the average each month for the last few years. You can then think of ways to lower that expense or eliminate it. This will relate to savings that you can also replicate with other expenses.

Homesteading is slowly setting yourself free from the usual monthly expenses. Most people have the following expenses to worry about each month:

- Mortgage or rent
- Insurance
- Taxes
- Gas
- Car payments
- Utilities
- Clothing, and
- Food

Rent or mortgage can be totally eradicated by buying a mobile home (for small-scale homesteaders) or purchasing a parcel of land (for large-scale homesteading). The former could cost as little as $5,000.

Property insurance will cost less when the value of the land is less. Total ownership of the assets will even free you from further expenses. You can also buy a used car instead of a brand-new one so you can pay for it in cash or set up easier monthly payments.

Think of the type of vehicles that you will need on your homestead. Keep in mind that you will need a pickup truck for the farm chores and a car with decent mileage. Older vehicles will greatly reduce tax and insurance costs. Many states have personal property tax assessments on vehicles annually. If you are not going to commute from your homestead to work, then you can save money on gas or diesel fuel.

As for the phone bills, find out which cell phone service provider will give you the most competitive plan. There are now Internet phones costing only $19.95 annually (minus Internet access).

This kind of low-cost phone or cell phone is most suitable for you if you need to save some more money. Check if there is rural Internet access in the area where you are moving. You might resort to satellite Internet if the cable, DSL, and telephone companies won't come out too far.

The costs are also still competitive, especially for the wireless offers for laptops. As for the electricity, you have the choice to use solar panels and other power sources, such as wind and water.

You can have a private well (or more) on your homestead. This could be a literal hole in the ground or one that is run by a good pump. You could install water filters so that your drinking water remains potable.

As of 2020, the cost for good drilling is $5,500 for a 150-foot depth. The price per project could vary, but the range could be anywhere from $1,500 up to $12,000. Residential water wells cost $15 to $25 per square foot, while agricultural or irrigation systems cost higher at $35 to $55 per square foot. An aquifer in place of an electric pump is estimated to be $25 to $45 per square foot.

If there is an existing well on your homestead, but you cannot fetch water from it anymore, then you could drill it again. The cost for re-drilling is $300 to $600 for the labor plus materials.

Growing your food is the most common motivation for many people to choose a life of homesteading. However, you have to consider gas expenses if you need to transport the harvested vegetables and fruits to places where you can sell or barter them.

Crafting also costs money, depending on what sort of crafting you will take on. Your options include hobby crafts such as crocheting, quilting, and knitting, or crafts that can add to your homesteading income, such as soap and candle making, paper crafts, essential oils production, and even sewing curtains.

Large or small, chickens cost less to feed when they roam freely within your protected area. The eggs that they lay can even be added to your items for bartering or kept for your consumption. There is less to zero fuss with these free-range chickens.

You can also raise rabbits for their meat. This is another affordable, healthy way to eat and provide for your family. For good quality hay, pellet, and fresh foods for your rabbit, an estimate is about $25 each month.

Raising dairy cows (costs between $2,000 and $5,000 per cow) and goats (price range is from $75 to $300) also reduce your reliance on commercial food vendors. With these animals, you can produce your own milk, ice cream, cheese, and butter. If you have more of them, you can even barter or sell so that you can purchase other goods with money.

And where there are livestock, fruits, and vegetables, there is also trash. Many homesteaders take their trash to transfer stations for free. For the less understanding local governments, there could be a minimal cost for trash pickup. The monthly trash collection cost can be $15 or so. This is an added convenience to your homesteading lifestyle, but you could choose differently by keeping a compost pit and learning to recycle.

One other major purchase that you need to prepare for so that you can formally begin your life as a homesteader is how to buy the perfect piece of land for homesteading.

You will learn this in a separate chapter.

# How to Avoid the BIGGEST Homesteading Mistakes

Okay, so you are ready to embrace the whole new level of freedom that homesteading offers. Those who have started before you know that it can be a trial and error process, but the more that you learn the basics, the better off you will be. And what better way is there to learn than to steer clear of the mistakes that were committed by other homesteaders?

## The Most Common Homesteading Errors

### Insufficient Research

Homesteading can look easy via its façade. You purchase chickens, place them in coops, and then you wish to collect their eggs and, eventually, their meats – but all this entails effort and time.

Be sure to do your research – lots of it – and interview homesteaders who have done it for years.

This book should provide the fundamentals of homesteading, so take the time to read and apply what you learn.

## Zero Planning

Since one of the necessary steps of any project is to start with a plan, not having one will definitely result in a disaster. Whether you just want to have a small yard or wide acres, it is crucial to begin with a plan.

Imagine not having a plan when you are faced with these issues:

- The number of animals that you can humanely and safely raise
- The cost of livestock farming
- The plants that grow best in your locality
- When to plant, etc.

You also need to set up a business plan before moving to the country. As you buy your acres of land, what would you support your family with? How will you pay the mortgage?

Will you sell your animals, or will you become a homesteading consultant? Are you going to be a homesteading blogger?

Whatever you plan to do, set up more than one thing because you need some form of income to support your new homestead.

## Expanding Too Soon

Making unrealistic plans is, technically, the opposite of not making plans at all. However, the downside to this, of course, is that people who have unrealistic plans do not even realize that they are impractical.

Idealism is great but not to the point of unfeasibility. You need to seriously assess if the goals that were set are really reachable. Also, consider if the timeframe that you set is even possible.

For instance, raising some chickens is realistic, but doing this on top of building a fence, building the coop, digging a well, and clearing the trees, all during the first week, just won't happen (unless you have additional human resources). This is the perfect recipe for burning out long before you even begin homesteading.

Break the goals down into smaller, more realistic tasks.

## Setting the Wrong Budget

There are some homesteaders who, in their excitement, must have calculated their homesteading budget incorrectly. The common problems that could arise from setting the wrong budget include:

- Not being able to buy enough seeds during planting season.

- Inability to cover expenses brought about by emergencies (e.g., human or livestock ailments and machinery and equipment repairs).

- Running short on income, especially when you decided to quit your job when you moved.

Budgeting ensures that you will be financially secure and free from debt (or, at the very least, have minimal debt) until you can fully depend on your homestead.

Since you will be learning about homesteading income sources later on, what you need to do, initially, is to create a monthly budget. A simple notebook and pen can be your tools, or you can use an Excel sheet or go on the Internet and look for apps that you can use to jump-start your budget planning.

Remember that every monthly budget should include the following:

- Recurring bills

- Upcoming/irregular bills (e.g., quarterly or annual bills)

- Seasonal or large purchases

- Loans, debt, mortgage, car payments, etc.

Set up the spreadsheet or make a chart in a notebook. Some people just use tables on a Word document.

Next, add all the income streams and deduct the monthly bills. Be sure to indicate the due dates so that you will not miss them. Be sure to set aside savings even when you are still paying off some debts.

Insert the formula on your Excel sheet or manually calculate the figures. Collect receipts so it will be easier to compute your expenses.

Never rely on your memory alone. It is better to keep records or take a photo using your phone camera each time that you make a purchase.

Recordkeeping is also not limited to accounting for your income and expenses.

You can keep records of the crops that you recently planted, livestock, harvested crops, and how much you were able to preserve.

Think of running your homestead as you would a business – you need to be on top of it no matter what. Never approach homesteading as a mere hobby because farming is a serious business. Every new project that is added to your homestead is, in essence, an investment.

### Zero Land Inspection

The problem with not evaluating the land that you are going to use for homesteading is that it might not produce the yield that you initially expected. Soil management is going to be a part of homesteading, and so you would want to physically inspect the land that you are going to invest in. The land, after all, is going to be the foundation of your upcoming homestead.

Take the time to research which states offer the best lands for homesteading. Some properties may look perfect during the summer but could be untamed during the other seasons.

Know your options and how much land you would need for your homesteading dream. There are country and farm estates to choose from, but do not assume that the zoning will automatically permit farm animals.

It is best to check first. Believe it or not, some rules allow horses but ban rabbits and chickens in certain estates. The closer your land is to the city, the likelier that you are going to have to deal with bylaws on livestock ownership.

Ask the locals about the property that you are considering. Check for running water sources and ample farming space.

### Buying Animals Before Building the Fence and Shelter

You are going to care about animals, so they are going to be your responsibility. Make sure that they have ample food, water, and shelter as well as protection from probable predators (e.g., bears, foxes, and wolves).

Many hobby farmers find small animals cute, so they bring them home as if every single one is going to be a pet – do not make this mistake.

Build a proper shelter and fence on your homestead and then add the goat shed, the rabbit hutch, and set up the rest of the barn.

Remember also to build the structures right the first time, or you will be fishing deep into your pocket for restructuring projects.

### Zero Breeding Knowledge

Are you going to sell the baby animals that the flock will produce?

You need to plan if you want to include breeding as a part of your homesteading. After all, it is not enough to have the courage to butcher your own animal or to possess the number of the local slaughterhouse. You also need to think about your potential customers and how to deal with the offspring once it is born.

Take note also of the animal feed costs, as these are recurring costs that you need to include in your budget. Furthermore, factor in the cost of gas, equipment, and your time even when you will make your own hay.

These beginner homesteading mistakes can be prevented. There is no need to agonize the way others before you have suffered. If you and your family are just starting out, then this book will help you start your homesteading journey more smoothly.

# PART TWO: LIVING OFF THE LAND

# Finding Land for Your Homestead

The majority of Americans believe that acres of crops and jam-packed feedlots are necessary to feed everybody. To many, large-scale agriculture with its GMOs and chemicals is needful just so that everyone will not starve to death. Even those who already know that doing agriculture the organic way produces the same results, believe it or not, are swayed to thinking otherwise.

But how much land is needed to feed the nation? How about a family?

As millions of farmers and owners of land would attest, this depends on the land quality as well as the size of the family that you need to support. You can grow food – everything that you need, in fact, on just a small piece of land.

You need to design a system that will work with natural processes to maximize food production. Developing the land for food production can start with as little as two acres (or even less).

Some principles and techniques can even grow food in as little as 25 percent of an acre. If people in the suburbs can live off their land, well, so can you.

Homesteading, as well as self-sufficiency, has become quite popular in recent years. However, the trend should in no way become your sole reason for joining the hundreds who have taken the plunge.

This book will guide you on how to jump-start your homesteading venture by learning intensive gardening strategies, even with less land. It will inspire you to become food-secure as soon as possible. It will prepare you for emergencies that are all realities of homesteading life, but before you set out to acquire the necessary skills and get your boots all muddied, how about buying a piece of land for your homestead first?

So how do you find the land that is perfect for your homesteading dream?

Browsing several real estate listings could get taxing even when you are merely looking for a traditional house – searching for a survival homestead is a different task altogether. Only a few real estate agents have the skills to answer your homesteading needs.

Before you make an appointment to look at a property, first, speak with your bank to ascertain that you are, indeed, ready for a loan. Ask how much your financial institution is willing to lend. Obtain a pre-approval letter before you even make price negotiations with the seller.

There are many options apart from a traditional home, so seek out the agents, preferably, those who are into homestead specific brokerages. If you are having difficulty finding a survival real estate agent in your locality, then find one who already has extensive experience in listing and then selling agricultural properties.

A lovely piece of farmland does not always translate into a survival homestead, so be sure to inspect your options more closely. Bucolic properties will surely be presented to you, and there are certain aspects of this kind of land that you need to scrutinize.

## Water Source

If the land – no matter how idyllic it may seem – does not even have a single natural water source, then have it removed from your potential homesteads. Look for a natural pond, spring, lake, or a creek or river frontage because these are the ideal and sustainable sources of homestead water.

If your potential homesteading land answers all your requirements except the water source, then have it shortlisted if its terrain could support one (or more) human-made ponds.

Check the age of the underground wells within the property and do this before making any offers to the seller. If there are no wells, then that is going to be an extra $15,000 to drill one.

If you plan on going off the grid, then you have to be able to fetch water, so be mindful of your water sources manually.

## Acreage

Do not be tempted by bargain prices. Take, for instance, fixer-upper farmland that has the potential to become a survival getaway. It could have all the acres that you need (plus some), but if half of it is wooded, and what you need is pastureland, then you have a lot of work to do to make the land adapt to your needs.

It is possible to grow and harvest ample food that can feed a family of four – many accomplished homesteaders have already done it – on a three-acre land (or even less). What you need are the skills to take control of the natural resources and put every single inch of the land to good use.

The ideal land size for a survival homestead is largely dependent on your family size, budget, skills, work availability, livestock types that are being raised, and natural attributes that are needed to sustain a farming lifestyle.

Building your food stock requires at least five acres of homestead land. Here, you will grow livestock such as rabbits, goats, and chickens. You can choose to add turkeys, ducks, pigs, and a cow.

## Gardening Plan

Yes, you will need to get used to planning. Plan the size of the garden that can feed your tribe. You need a more extensive design if you want to have a month of the stockpile, and now, with a visual representation of the potential land right before your eyes, you will be better able to draft gardening strategies.

Consider also if you will grow a traditional garden or a vertical one. Will it be necessary to build a greenhouse? Plan where you will situate the garden. As much as possible, make it completely hidden from the road and your neighbors.

Imagine having a long-term disaster, and with your garden in plain view, it could easily become the target for marauders or your neighbors with a starving child.

Get a soil sample also before you sign the contract. Check if the topsoil is sandy, clay, or loam. Make sure that it can sustain the vibrant greens that you see during the inspection.

## A Refuge

At the end of the day, the land that you are going to purchase is where you will live, so be able to define what you want. Find land near your home. If you are attached to your local culture, then, by all means, stay there. If your happiness is defined by a sense of community, then find a place with a culture and language that are familiar to you and your family.

Brett R. McLeod, Ph.D. from Antioch University in England, believes in the power of connectivity and localized lifestyle as an alternative to the popular consumer culture.

Visualize the habitat that you will create. Would you want to pick apples and oranges? Would you want to milk your cows? Would you preserve foods in your pantry? The natural, innate tendencies of land may be difficult to assess at first glance, but research will greatly help. Remember that when humans fight nature, more often than not, the latter always wins.

Look for overgrown and weedy fields, neglected lots, choppy terrains, and out-of-the-way spots. The general climate in the area also matters. If you love the sub-tropical heat of California or Florida, then that is the best place for you to set up your homestead.

Visit the courthouse and search for maps. Take time to familiarize yourself with the region's watersheds and topography. Would you prefer flat land or one with rolling hills?

Talk to the locals, such as the farmers, vendors, the feed store owners, delivery personnel, and potential neighbors.

All in all, do not rely on real estate ads – only believe what you see and hear. Ask around and shop around. Inspect roads and look for areas with people who do a bit of farming. Keep in mind that large, cleared lands that can accommodate giant tractors are going to be pricey, and those that are already used in farming might have soils that are saturated with chemicals.

Sometimes the answer to your homesteading requirements sits, neglected, in an abandoned space, so keep an open mind.

### Free Land

The depopulation in rural communities, brought on by the influx of people seeking jobs in cities, is now slowly being reversed by the homesteading trend. Free land is now being offered to prospective residents in the following states:

### Alaska

Land here is being sold for private ownership and settlement. There is also a program where applicants are allowed to stake a piece of land in a remote area set aside, specifically, for recreation use. These parcels of land are leased for a limited time, and the applicants have a chance to buy them at fair market value after an appraisal and survey.

There is no need to fulfill prove-up or building requirements – you can apply for this program so long as you are a resident of Alaska.

# Iowa

Free land is also offered to families who can build a residence in specified lots. The Manilla Economic Development Corporation makes the offer at zero cost for families and individuals.

Marne, IA, also offers free lands averaging 80' x 120'. You may apply via the town's website.

# Kansas

There are a handful of communities in this state that are offering free land to draw potential residents. Most of this land is serviced municipal lots that are just right for gardening but may not be best for full-scale farming.

There are also restrictions on house size as well as the time that you need to finish building. Find opportunities in Lincoln, Mankato, Marquette, Tescott, and Osborne.

# Minnesota

New Richland offers 86' x 130' land to anyone interested in constructing a new home in just one year. The town has a free land website that you can visit.

# Nebraska

The city of Beatrice gives away city land to any individual or family who is willing to construct a home and then live in that home for three years (Homestead Act of 2010).

So far, the program has proven to be successful. Other towns are also offering free land as well as other incentives for their new residents. Find opportunities in Curtis, Central City, Giltner, Elwood, Kenesaw, Juniata, and Loup City. Get in touch with these towns' municipal offices to consider your options.

# Other Opportunities

These could also present as rural homes with owners who have to move to assisted living communities. These owners may be looking for future occupants or for people who would want to care for the property at the moment. Think of caretaking as your foot in the door.

Look also for cooperative opportunities. Some large-scale homesteaders might not even be able to afford their lands, were it not for their shared arrangements with other homesteading families.

Cooperative living is not a new arrangement, although it may not be as common as city and town housing co-ops.

Shared garden and orchard spaces are practical means to grow your food initially. You can choose to opt-out later on or be like some of the homesteaders who have stayed in co-op lands for decades.

Lastly, before you put up cash, you also need to check the following:

● Property access rights (make sure that you have legal, permanent transferrable access specified, to the letter, in the deed).

● Sewer and drainage matters.

● Mineral rights (you would want to stipulate what will serve as your compensation should coal or any kind of mineral be discovered on your property).

● Timber rights (check how much timber is granted to you until the land is already paid for).

● Land easements (of course, you would not want to build a vegetable garden right in the middle of a neighbor's right-of-way).

● Permits and zoning.

Protect yourself in all aspects – this is the basic rule to search for that perfect piece of land. Have every transaction recorded at the public registry – as the saying goes, *better safe than sorry.*

# Growing Your Own Food

Growing fruits and vegetables need not be overwhelming. It also offers many benefits, whether you are just tending a backyard garden or have committed to a life of farming.

Eating fresh is one of the leading reasons to grow and harvest your own food. You can help improve your family's health as you grow food in your backyard. The vitamin content of these foods will be at their highest levels because they come straight from your garden.

Another reason to grow fruits and vegetables is so you can save some money on groceries. One seed packet costs less than a dollar, but it has the power to shrink your grocery bill later on.

Gardening can also help the planet in so many ways, especially when you decide to say "no" to herbicides and pesticides. Through you – no matter how small your initial contribution would be –, there would be less water and air pollution.

All the weeding, planting, watering, and eventual harvesting are physical activities that can also serve as your outdoor exercise, so go right ahead and start gardening.

# The Garden Soil

Soil is a crucial factor for every successful garden, regardless of the kind of garden that you plan to grow. It will take time and research to find the right kind of soil, test it, and then finally use it to grow your plants.

There are two extreme soil textures – sandy and clay soils. Coarser sand particles are known as gravel. Touch it, and it will easily crumble. Clay soil, on the other hand, is smoother. When wet, clay is sticky and will easily smear like paint.

When clay and sand are mixed, this is the ideal soil for gardening, which is known as loam. Sandy loam permits the drainage of surplus water while clay loam holds water. Remember that the ideal gardening soil has equal parts of water and air.

When you hear about organic matter, this is simply the vegetable and animal matter that is undergoing the decomposition process. Adding humus offers little amounts of chemicals that are needed for plant growth. There is also ample food for the bacteria in the soil, which, in turn, provides organic chemicals to the growing plants.

Humus is what you need to keep the garden soil porous and open. This allows water and air to penetrate the soil, while also acting as a sponge that keeps the roots healthy so they can hold nutrients.

## What Else Do Your Plants Need?

Plants need carbon, oxygen, and hydrogen in order to grow. They get all these from water and air together with the soil. They also need phosphorus, nitrogen, and potassium that can be supplied by fertilizers.

Other needful elements are magnesium, sulfur, iron, and calcium. These are readily available in most soils. Trace elements like zinc, manganese, boron, copper, and molybdenum can be added in minute quantities.

All these elements must be present, as insoluble forms, in the soil as well as the water and air.

There are three elements that every fertilizer must have so that it can be classified as complete: nitrogen, potassium, and phosphorus. Take note that, by law, the amounts that the fertilizer contains of each element must be clearly indicated on the package. If boron is added, then the number will also be indicated on the packaging.

Nitrogen is derived from slaughterhouse by-products like bone and blood, phosphorus is processed from phosphate rock, and potassium comes from wood ashes.

Another thing that you also need to check concerning the soil is whether it is acidic or alkaline. Garden soil can be either or neutral. Most vegetable and fruit plants thrive in neutral or moderately acidic soil. There are even plants that demand acidic soil, while fewer plants demand sweet or alkaline soil.

You also need to check the subsoil that is the layer right beneath the surface. It can be just a few inches down, or it could go as deep as 20 inches. This can be full of gravel or sand; that is why you need to check how deep this layer is as plants only get the nutrients from the topsoil.

Sandy or clay subsoil is difficult to work with because it requires a drainage system. Sandy subsoil can, however, be corrected by adding peat moss, manure, and organic matter. Planting green manure crops such as oats, rye, ryegrass, clover, and vetch can also improve sandy subsoil.

Other ways to improve the soil is to mix sand with clay soil and vice versa. An application of mixed cow and horse manure (about two-three inches thick) is the fastest method to improve the soil and add plant foods. The manure has to be partially rotten already.

Use sheep and chicken manure only when mixed with compost or dried leaves. If manure is hard to get, green manure and peat moss are good alternatives.

### The Compost Pile

The foundation of a compost pile is comprised of the following:

1. Dead stems and stalks of corn, marigold, and zinnia stay at the bottom.

2. The next layer is six-inch deep grass cutting made with dead leaves, rotting peels and fruits, and vegetable wastes.

3. Next, a three-inch deep garden soil.

4. The fourth layer is a 3-6" deep peat moss.

5. Lime

6. Manure

7. The top layer is the complete fertilizer.

Starting at the second layer, repeat the sequence until the heap has reached four-six feet. The sides of the heap should be sloping inward, with the top left part depressed to hold water.

Upon completion, the pile should be watered. Make sure that every layer is saturated with water, but not to the point of overflowing.

## Things you can add to your compost pile:

- Dog, fish, or cat food
- Fur from brushing the dogs
- Alfalfa hay
- Bee droppings
- Cow, horse, or goat manure
- Aquarium plants
- Bird droppings
- Fish scraps
- Horsehair
- Feathers

Apart from the pet stuff, you can also add laundry room things such as:

- Dryer lint

- Shredded denim or cotton clothing
- Shredded old towels
- Shredded old socks

**Kitchen items that can also be thrown onto the pile:**

- Paper napkins
- Paper towels
- Vegetables that have been freezer burned
- Teabags
- Cooked rice and pasta
- Coffee grounds
- Coffee filters
- Stale cereal
- Stale chips, bread, and crackers
- Chopped wine corks
- Nutshells, except walnuts
- Shredded cardboard and food boxes
- Popcorn
- Stale beer
- Old spices
- Old wine
- Eggshells
- Outdated yogurt
- Corn cobs
- Paper receipts
- Leftover salads
- Chopped up seeds
- Pizza crusts

- Any paper wrapper

**Even office trash can be added to the compost pile:**

- Shredded papers and bills
- Sticky notes
- Pencil shavings
- Paper envelopes (now the window type ones)
- Matte business cards

**And, of course, household items that you can also turn into compost:**

- Newspapers
- Used potpourri
- Contents of a vacuum cleaner
- Houseplant leaves
- Dried flowers from vases
- Fireplace ashes
- Used tissue paper
- Shredded toilet paper and their cardboard tubes
- Old leather gloves
- Shredded old sheets
- Glue
- Razor trimming
- Leather wallets and watch bands
- Scraps of Ivory soap
- Cotton balls
- Greeting cards
- Used matches
- Fingernail and toenail clippings

# Fruits and Vegetables

There is nothing like enjoying a fresh bowl of hand-tossed salad with the ingredients picked from your garden. To begin enjoying these freshly picked vegetables, you need to find the right location that gets ample sunlight during the day but also has shade during the hottest parts of the afternoon. The shading could be any permanent structure or a towering tree. You can also use shade cloth if you do not have either.

For small spaces, you can grow your vegetable garden vertically. The best plants that benefit from vertical growth are: beans, peas, cucumbers, vining flowers, small squash, and tomatoes.

You will need a trellis (wooden or metal bars used to support climbing plants) for these vegetables so you can better prune and harvest them.

Growing vegetables in pots is also a thing in many apartments and tiny homes. You can begin with these for now, and then you could eventually look for an empty neighborhood lot that you can convert to a community garden.

Even newbies can start planting fast-growing vegetables soon. The shorter the time between the planting and harvest times, the more fast-growing the vegetable variety is.

Other factors that influence a vegetable's growth are sunlight, soil nutrients, ample water, and the time and energy that you put into caring for them. Now, would you like to learn the easiest vegetables to plant in your new garden?

## Zucchini

This is, perhaps, the most fail-proof vegetable to grow on your homestead. This is a low-maintenance plant that grows in almost any kind of soil and climate. It's the perfect SHTF crop.

Do not let it grow too big, though. Freeze any excess crops for later use in baking bread and preparing soups and sauces.

Zucchini can also be grown on rooftop gardens (great for apartment homesteaders) and in pots.

## Greens

Remember the leafy greens like lettuce, kale, arugula, and spinach because they are awesome for beginner homesteaders. These mature in as little as three-four weeks; to harvest, just snip the tops or pick some leaves.

Spinach is a delicious crop that grows best in cool weather, so it is best to plant the initial crop four weeks before the final frost date and then the second crop about six-eight weeks after the final frost date. You can harvest spinach in as early as 20 days. Just pick the outer leaves so you can continuously harvest into the season.

Kale, on the other hand, is a nutritious, sweet-tasting green that is also best planted during the cooler weather. It can even grow during winter. A spring crop can be planted four weeks before the last frost date, with the second crop planted in late summer or the start of fall. You can harvest kale in 60 days when it has fully matured. Young leaves can also be harvested before this, but be sure to leave four or more leaves so that it can still grow.

Arugula has a unique taste that is best used in salad and sometimes with chicken and other meat varieties. Plant the arugula just a few weeks before the last frost date and then the second crop during fall. As soon as you see flowers, remove them so that the plant can grow further. It only takes 20 days for the young leaves to develop – 40 days if you want a mature harvest.

Lettuce is a salad staple, but it is also an awesome leafy green that can be included in any kind of diet. Just like its cousins, it grows best in cold weather, so plant the spring crops about four weeks before the last frost date. The fall crops can be planted at about four weeks before the initial frost date.

Lettuce takes 40 days to mature, although you can harvest leaves even when they are still small.

## Beans

These vegetables are nutritionally charged foods that can be eaten in different ways. They are easily dried, edible even when raw, and they are a staple in any vegetable garden.

Plant beans when you're sure that the soil is going to be consistently warm. Many beans mature in just 60 days, although some can take as long as a hundred days. Farmers prefer to use a trellis when growing beans for greater support and tastier fruits.

## Snap Peas

This is a prolific producer. Peas come in different varieties, but the snap peas are great for starter homesteads because they can grow all-year-round. Plant them one-two weeks before the last frost date. Harvest within 40-60 days.

## Green Onions

These crops do not just add flavor to your meals; they are also highly nutritious. Just like the snap peas, green onion prefers warmer soil, so make sure that the last frost date has passed before you plant it.

It only takes 50 days to mature so you can uproot it then; although, you can harvest the stalks in between. Limit your stalk harvests as these can restrict the bulb's growth.

## Carrots

These root crops need loose, sandy soil, so take it easy using manure type fertilizers when you plant them. It is best to plant lots of carrots as growing them can be a tad tricky. They are a great practice crop for you, though, since their growth happens away from your site.

Plant carrots four weeks before the last frost date and then harvest 60 days after.

## Turnips

An excellent source of antioxidants and fiber, this root crop is a tough and reliable garden staple. Some use it as a substitute for potatoes.

Plant it three weeks before the last frost date then harvest in spring. You can plant again in September for your fall harvest. It only takes 30-60 days to mature, with turnip greens harvested in 30 days and the mature crops in 60 days.

### Tomatoes

But what's a homestead without a patch of tomatoes?

Wait for 60 days before you can harvest. This is after planting after the last frost date in spring and then pruning every seven-ten days.

### Corn

If you have bigger land, then you can have stocks of cornmeal ground from your own corn plants. The sweet variety can be eaten right away, canned, or even frozen.

Since this is your first time, buy seeds from the market and then plant with a 20 to 30-inch row space. Plant about 33,000-38,000 seeds in every acre. Increase the rate, and you can maximize the corn yield.

Always check the weather report. Plant a small amount during the dry season and more during the wetter months. Scientifically, the temperature should be no less than 50 degrees Fahrenheit. Make sure that there are going to be five to 14 days of warm days ahead. The soil's moisture must not be wet, or it will be too compacted, and the corn will not grow.

Add organic fertilizers according to your plants' needs. If the soil is fertile, then there is no need to do so.

## Medicinal Herbs

Herbs are useful plants that can boost everyone's health and wellness. Most of these are not difficult to plant; there are many with lovely flowers and unique foliage. They can also be easily infused in any garden bed; in fact, some can grow pretty well in pots.

The basic arsenal would be garlic, basil, and mint – start small, so it will be hard to miss. All these are also used in cooking, so you are fulfilling both gastronomic and wellness needs.

**You can start with:**

- Ginger
- Licorice root
- Ginseng
- Myrrh
- Fennel
- Walnut

## And what about fruits?

### Berries

Blackberries, blueberries, and raspberries are all fruits that are rich in antioxidants. These are considered superfoods because of their nutritional values.

Black cherries are great liquor and jam ingredients. The tree grows quickly at two-three years, so you definitely have something to look forward to.

It can take one-three years for the bushes to produce their first fruits, but you can harvest annually after that. So, without a doubt, berries are a good investment for year-round consumption.

### Other Fast-Growing Fruit Trees

Fig trees are known to bear fruit after only one-two years of planting. They are easy to grow and can even be planted in pots when you live in colder regions.

Mulberries are known to produce fruits in just one year. You can also share this with the ducks, chickens, and turkeys.

Peaches can produce fruits in less than three years. What they require is well-drained soil and a partner so they can cross-pollinate.

Citrus trees can be grown in pots should you have limited gardening space. Choose from oranges, lemons, and limes. These are self-pollinating, so there is no need to worry about buying a pair to produce fruits.

These are the basic vegetables and fruits that you can plant with your starter garden. Remember that you can begin gardening even with just a small parcel of land.

Live in an apartment? Then find a bucket and start planting. There is simply no excuse – the best time to enjoy the blessings of homesteading is now.

# 21 Homestead Gardening Hacks

Now that you learned which vegetables and fruits are the easiest to plant and harvest, you are sure to reap the blessings of your hard work soon. In the meantime, here are some homesteading hacks that will further increase your harvest.

### #1. Use Wood Pallets

These old pallets can be turned into vertical gardens or raised beds. Those who have smaller acres of land or are just homesteading in their backyards would do well to grow peas, peppers, lettuce, basil, mint, and even cucumbers using old wooden pallets.

### To make a raised garden bed, you will need:

- Wooden pallets
- Topsoil
- Scissors
- Garden fabrics
- Staple gun with staples
- Seeds and plants

### Method:

1. Clean the pallets and then turn them over.

2. Lay the fabric across the back of the wooden pallet.

3. Staple the sides, making sure that the fabric is taut.

4. Turn the pallet over and check for any holes where dirt could leak.

5. Fill the pallet beds with topsoil from your garden or a mixture of prime soils that you bought.

6. Start planting as you would in a regular garden.

## #2. Hang Shiny Pots, CDs, and DVDs

Believe it or not, keeping squirrels and birds away from your fruit trees is as easy as gathering some old CDs and DVDs and then hanging them right on the tree. These dangling discs will reflect light and act as prisms so that the birds will think that a larger animal is already present.

Squirrels do not like the reflecting light, so they stay away from such trees.

## #3. Pinch off the Top

While it is awfully tempting to grow your herbs and vegetables to full maturity, it pays if you pinch off the top stems now and then. This simple action encourages further growth because the dormant leaves are signaled to grow outwards.

## #4. Use Kitchen Scraps

If you still have not started a compost heap, then put those kitchen scraps to good use. Throw the scraps (minus citrus fruits and fatty meats) into the blender, add a bit of water, and then mix away. This mixture will easily decompose so you can then put it at the base of plants.

## #5. Add a Drop of Oil

You can prevent mosquitoes and other insects from breeding when you add just a few vegetable oil drops to the water. This will form a thin layer over the water surface that will deter the insects but will not harm the birds.

Use this method on your water barrels and birdbaths.

## #6. Dwarf the Fruit Trees

By now, you already know that you do not need huge amounts of land to grow vegetables and fruits. There are now dwarf fruit trees that you can plant even inside your home.

Growing these fruit tree varieties will even allow you to take care of non-native fruits. Choose from dwarf orange, apple, coffee, banana, and lemon.

## #7. Fertilize with Poultry

Duck and chicken manure make good fertilizer. As you prep the plots for your garden, you could set up a temporary pen for the chickens. They can be kept in there for a week (up to two) depending on the plot size. The chickens will naturally fertilize the soil while they also peck at pests.

You can also collect rabbit droppings by creating a tub filled with dirt. Place this underneath the hutches. What you collect will become a nutrient-rich soil that can be used as seed starters.

## #8. Create Rain Barrel Systems

Homesteaders prefer to have rainwater harvested because tap water potentially has high levels of chlorine. You can even save a huge amount of money since you can collect as much as 300 gallons of rainwater for every inch of rain on a 500-square-foot roof.

To make your rain barrel system, prepare these materials:

- A large plastic garbage bin (or more)
- A tube of sealant or Teflon tape
- Two rubber washers
- One hose clamp
- One spigot
- Drill
- Landscaping fabric

## Method:

1. Drill a hole in the garbage bin. This is where the spigot will be inserted. Be sure to use a drill bit that is smaller than the spigot's size. Do not place the hole too low into the bin so that there will still be ample space underneath to fill the barrel.

2. Insert the spigot after placing a metal washer into its threaded end. Fit with a rubber washer on the threads so that the washer is held in place. Check for holes that could potentially leak.

3. Seal the rubber washer with a waterproof sealant. Make sure that the spigot is secured with a hose clamp so that it won't come loose from the rainwater barrel.

4. Create a hole that will gather the rainwater from the downspout. Drill another hole at the top where the rainwater can overflow.

5. If you do not want to waste overflow water, then you can connect a PVC pipe or hose to another barrel. This way, any excess water will run to the following barrel.

6. Cut the landscaping fabric and place it over the top of the barrel. This will serve as a barrier against mosquitoes and other insects that could get into your rainwater barrel.

7. Put the lid on, then close it.

8. Place the rain barrel underneath the downspout then wait for the rains to fall.

### #9. Use Toilet Paper Tubes as Seed Starters

These tubes are biodegradable, and they come at the right size for seeds to grow in. To use, cut flaps on one end of the tube then close it off. This can then be used as a home for your starting seeds.

### #10. Reuse Coffee Grounds

Old coffee grounds can be used to enrich the garden soil while it also deters aphids from damaging your leafy greens.

## #11. Make Beer Traps

Beer can be used as a trap for garden snails and slugs. Have a shallow dish filled with beer then put these in your garden. The scent of the fermented liquid will lure the slugs into the dish. While they can climb into the drink, they will not be able to ascend out of the trap.

## #12. Plant Densely

Apart from aphids and slugs, one other thing that you wouldn't want growing in your garden is weeds. To keep them from appearing in the first place, you can plant densely on the garden beds. Mother Nature does not like gaps, so she quickly fills any empty spot. Plant densely, and there would be no room for the weeds to grow in.

## #13. Find Uses for Wood Ash

As you drive away the garden pests, you can also use wood ash to fertilize your growing vegetables and fruits. This is packed with potassium, calcium, magnesium, phosphorus, sodium, iron, and zinc. To use, dust it over the plant bases or place it together with other compost ingredients.

Creating a chicken run using an old tire filled with wood ash will also keep the hens from being bored while keeping mite infestation to a bare minimum.

## #14. Grow Roots with Honey

Honey can also be used as a root grower. Instead of purchasing rooting hormones, you can apply honey on the plant cuttings. Its antibacterial properties will help in propagating the roots more quickly.

## #15. Use Packing Peanuts in Large Pots

Instead of filling up large pots with pure potting soil, try mixing it with packing peanuts. You will use less soil while improving the water drainage. You will also find that the pot has become lighter the moment you decide to move it.

## #16. Never Dig Wet Soil

Soil is not just difficult to dig when it is wet. Digging wet will also guarantee that it will be compacted (this is not good for gardening). If the soil sticks to your boots' soles when you go out and dig, then postpone the task to a drier day.

## #17. Keep Rust at Bay

To protect your gardening tools from rust, use a bucket or a big terracotta pot. Fill it with abrasive sand with some mineral oil. Place your tools into the bucket once you're done gardening. The abrasion and oil will keep them sharp, clean, and lubricated.

## #18. Soak the Seeds Before Planting

This is an effective way to germinate seeds quickly. Soak them overnight before planting them. Do not soak for more than 12 hours, though, because this will result in decomposition rather than faster germination.

## #19. Diapers for Water Retention

If you live in a region with a hot climate, then this hack is especially useful to you. Place a clean diaper (with the absorbent side up) at the bottom of a garden pot. Fill the pot with soil, put in your plant, and then water.

## #20. Apple Cider Vinegar as a Supplement

One of the best ways to boost your livestock's immune system is to add some apple cider vinegar to their food or water during winter. You soon see that the animal/s will be less sickly or will not suffer from infections as you boost their immune system naturally.

## #21. Rotate the Crops

Crop rotation is the process of growing certain vegetables in specific plots every year. An example is when you plant brassicas right after planting legumes the previous planting season. Since the legumes will have already added nitrogen to the ground, then the brassicas will greatly benefit from the nutrient.

Crop rotation avoids the depletion of soil nutrients.

These are just 21 mind-blowing gardening hacks that you can start practicing in your quest to getting more involved in the cycle of life. So, are you now ready to learn about livestock farming?

# Self-Sufficient Farming: What Livestock and How Many?

Throughout the centuries, farmers all over the globe have developed various livestock breeds. One breed (or even more) becomes extinct with each passing month, with 20 percent of the world's population of pigs, cattle, goats, horses, and poultry breeds now at risk of extinction.

If you went back in history, you would see that farmers used to operate in smaller acreages. Though this was the case, they still took care of a wide variety of animal and plant species. And the breeds that were developed often answered specific needs.

The Texas Longhorn is an example of a breed of cattle that was developed from Spanish cattle. These arrived during the earliest colonization days of North America. The ranchers then needed tough cattle that could live through predator pressure, poor forage, and still be able to produce healthy calves.

The unique horns soon emerged and were useful in fending off predators.

There is no need to create a unique breed in your homestead now. What you need to learn is to look for the animal breeds that will be productive and sustainable. The livestock farming tips that you will learn here are general guidelines only. If you live in an arid region, then Ossabaw Island pigs are perfect animals to grow on your homestead. Looking for chickens that can lay eggs even during the harshest winters? Then raise Chanticleer chickens as livestock.

# Animals You Can Raise on Your Large Homestead

## Rabbits

Rabbit meat is tasty and has low cholesterol. The animal can be raised even in a small backyard, and unlike chickens that need special equipment to be raised, the rabbit is not only cheaper to feed, but it also does not require a huge space. It should be confined, though, so that no predators can get near it.

Rabbit hutches must be built above the ground so that skunks and dogs are kept at bay.

If you want to harvest more than the rabbit meat, then you can also use the fur. The rabbit pelt has been worn for years. Angora rabbits can shed enough fur to make a coat.

Make sure that the hutches can effectively protect the rabbits from snow, rain, and predators, such as dogs and skunks. For warmth, you can add straw or some bedding materials to the hutches.

Note that a full-time rabbit business should have 600 does and around 60 bucks. Every doe gives birth to 25-50 live rabbits every year. To feed a family of five who wants to consume rabbit three times each week, you should have 12-13 fryers (baby rabbits) per month.

# Goats

Modern homesteaders can attest to the level of self-sufficiency that this livestock can provide. You can now have stocks of cheese and milk provided by your dairy goats.

Note that the goats need to give birth to kids so that they will lactate. You can then milk them throughout the year (for up to three years). You can plan and stagger the kidding so that you will have milk throughout the year.

One average-size dairy goat can provide three-four quarts of milk every day. Depending on the goat milk's butterfat content, you can even get up to one pound of cheese for every gallon of milk.

You can also raise goats for their fur. Called fiber goats, they can provide yarns that can be spun as blankets, hats, sweaters, and other items. Spinners pay for goat fibers, so while you put the weed-killing abilities of this livestock to good use, you even earn money from the fibers that you sell.

Build durable fences when you want to raise goats. Use woven wire, cattle panels, or welded wire. The fence should be no less than four feet high. Tighten the materials so that the goats cannot destroy them. A strand of electric wire can be strung across the top of the fence.

Every goat needs 200 square feet of fenced run. This is the minimum, so you can make room for your goats to roam and play. They also need a constant supply of fresh water.

Does, bucks/billys, and pregnant goats need about three cups of feed every day. When being milked, allow the goat to eat more than this. Wethers eat less than a cup.

Goats prefer weed, hay, and alfalfa. Forage should be a part of their diet, including leaves, dandelions, and weeds.

Make sure your goats have ample vitamins and minerals, too. Their vitamins are not the same as sheep, so check the labels. They also need routine care, such as worming, hoof trimming, and vaccinations (especially for tetanus).

One to two goats can easily provide an annual supply of fresh milk for a family of five. To grow your goat livestock, you can start with two does and one ram. Double this population if you have a bigger family to sustain.

## Sheep

Sheep are great for wool harvests, meat provision, and milk production. If you have goats, then you have, technically, enough training to raise sheep. They are alike in terms of their shelter and fence requirements.

Salt blocks are great sources of minerals for sheep. Fresh water is also a must, so if you can, set up a water station for the sheep.

Sheep cannot consume copper - this is poisonous to them.

General care for them includes trimming their hooves, shaving their wool, worming, and checking for other parasites.

It is suggested that a large family would begin with two ewes and one ram. This can eventually be grown to four ewes.

## Pigs

These are a great addition to any homestead because they eat up the often problematic kitchen leftovers, plus they provide delicious pork. Just like goats, they constantly break fences in their need to escape.

They are easier to farm compared to cattle, though, because they require the lowest maintenance. They do not need immunizations, they don't have to be milked, there's no need to sheer them, and you don't even have to be that hands-on.

Provide them with ample feed and water, and you're good to go. Make sure that they are also fenced in together with their big buddies.

A pair of pigs would be enough for families with six-eight members.

# Cows

Here is something to wow you - a thousand-pound cattle averages 430 pounds of steaks, ground beef, roasts, stew beef, etc. This should feed about 430 people who would consume one-pound serving each.

You can raise cows for meat and milk. Calves can also be sold to homesteaders like you. Eventually, even their hide can be turned into something useful. For many farmers and homesteaders, this is dream livestock. Prepare yourself because these are bigger animals, so they require a larger space and infrastructure that can contain them.

Getting a cow requires an upfront cost. You also need to prepare for the maintenance that it will need.

Now the question to ask yourself is: "Why will I raise a cow?"

You need to know your goals. Raising the cows solely for milk will be costly. First, they begin producing milk when they are two years and older or when they have their first calf. After the colostrum (first milk) is given to the calf, the cow can then be milked for two years.

Raw milk is rarely sold in retail stores - only a few states allow its sales. If you live in one of the 20 states that consider unpasteurized milk sales to be illegal (e.g., Alabama, Virginia, Colorado, etc.), then it will not be feasible to earn much money from milking.

A single cow can provide you more milk than what you can normally consume. But if you are only buying two gallons of milk at $3 apiece, then you're not saving a lot there.

You could make more money if you raise the cow and eventually sell it.

For homesteaders who purchase cows for their homegrown meat, it is necessary to find a meat processor or custom slaughterers. Grass-fed cows are ready to be slaughtered in 28-30 months while the grain-fed breed is ready in 15-16 months.

Invest in stock or a heifer that weighs 600-700 pounds. It will grow during the summer, and then it will be ready to be stocked in your freezer by fall. It can be challenging to process the meat since qualified processors are few. Schedule a slot for the slaughter date way before it happens.

If you plan on selling beef, then you also have to research your potential markets. You have to label and safely process the meat before you can sell it. Remember that meat is generally more lucrative than milk.

Different breeds of cows thrive in different climates. The hot climate of Florida or Texas will make the Brahman cow thrive. Red Angus will live in North Carolina.

Raise the Angus breed, Belted Galloway, or Hereford (all small breeds) if you live in an area where feed is pricey. Always buy cows from reputable breeders and feed from trustworthy suppliers.

One cow needs about an acre of land. Once they begin having calves, then you need two acres for each cow-calf duo. Check the forage quality on your land. You might need to add supplements to their diet if the forage quality is poor.

Feed the cows with grass and legumes and then balance their diet with mineral supplements. Vetch is also good in winter. If you want to add grains, then use high-protein corns.

Just like goats, they also need a constant supply of fresh water.

### Fowls

Ducks' space requirements depend on the breed that you are going to raise. Larger breeds, such as Saxony or Jumbo Pekin, would do well in a space of four-five square feet. For them to be able to run around, you will need to set up a minimum of ten square feet for every duck.

Pekins are heavy, so they are also highly recommended for homesteaders who worry that they will fly away during winter. These are also wonderful foragers, so they grow up to a size that will provide ample meat for the family.

You can also create a small pond so they can splash around. If this is not feasible at the moment, then allow a few ducks to share the kiddie pool.

Be sure to keep any fowl livestock protected. Ducks are commonly preyed upon. Even your dog might chase the ducks, so prepare for this scenario. Place a fence all around the area where the ducks are supposed to roam.

Hawks will have a hard time going into the fenced area since they need to swoop down instead of lower themselves like a helicopter.

Wooden pallets can be set up as duck houses. They are perfect for airflow and moisture. Build them low to the ground so that the ducks will be enticed to use them.

Ducks rise earlier than chickens, are hardier, and lay bigger eggs. They do not lay eggs throughout the year, though, so enjoy the fresh duck eggs while they are being provided to you.

Another type of fowl that you can raise on a homestead is the goose. Just like the ducks, you need to keep the geese happy if you want to harvest ample meat. They are easy to care for, they eat less than ducks and chickens, and they feed mostly on grass and then some corn and oats during winter.

You can simply let nature take its course when you purchase a pair of mature adults (two years old or older). They are monogamous animals, so the gander will often pair with just two female geese. Let them live together for a few months so they can begin to mate.

When properly mated, a female can lay 20 eggs in spring. She will only be able to hatch 12 to 15. You can take six-eight of her eggs and help the female hatch them using an incubator. As goslings are hatched, it could take as long as 24 hours for each one to break out of the shell. Never help it.

Goslings and other geese should be transferred to the fenced run as soon as they can mingle. Set up a fence that is no taller than three feet. If you have a dog that constantly preys on them, then raise the fence higher.

The geese can weed out a strawberry patch so you can fence them in there. Keep them out of there once the strawberry fruits begin to ripen. Keep them safe from foxes, owls, and raccoons.

The myth that geese need a large pond or lake to survive on a homestead had been long busted. You don't even need a huge body of water to keep the birds.

Just set up a trough for the goslings and the adult birds to splash in now and then and also for them to drink from occasionally. Geese forage for bugs and grass, so they do not need supplements, except during their first few weeks of life and in winter.

Geese varieties include the Chinese watchdog breed. They are elegant, but they are quite noisy. The Embden variety could weigh as much as 26 pounds, and they produce large eggs.

The Toulouse variety can also weigh as much as the Embden. At breeding age, they can be worth $100-150 each, so when they are sold in pairs, they could give you good amounts of cash.

Quails can also be a part of your large-scale homestead. The common breed – Bobwhite – matures in just 16 weeks, which means you can have quail meat in just four months. They lay eggs at 24 months.

Quails do not require much space. A two feet by two feet by eight feet pen could house as many as 25 quails. Invest in an incubator if you want to profit from quail eggs and meat.

Note that there is a special chapter dedicated to raising backyard chickens.

You will need about two gallons or more of water, every day, for a dozen turkeys. A 4' long waterer can sustain up to 12 birds. A hundred pounds of feed should be good enough for a dozen of them. By the time that the birds mature, though, you will already need to feed them a pound of feed, each, daily.

# Bees

Becoming an apiarist (beekeeper) means understanding the biology of these insects. Unfertile female bees are the workers while the queen lays the eggs. There are just a few drones (drones) in the hive. Every worker lives for six weeks, and then she simply dies from working herself to death. Every worker will have gathered nectar that can make a 1/12 teaspoon of honey.

Rev. L.L. Langstroth first conceptualized the modern beehive in 1851. Before this, farmers just left the bees in hollow logs, boxes, or straw keeps. The bees are eventually killed or violently ripped out of the honeycomb. Langstroth made movable frames as well as uniform bee spaces. The interiors have sections that are separated by 5/16". A homesteader can then harvest honey without damaging their home or hurting them.

You can buy established hives from expert beekeepers. This could cost anywhere from $50 to $100. Never buy a colony that has not been inspected by the state department of agriculture or an apiarist (beekeeper).

You can also have bees delivered by mail. The three-pound box can be delivered to your homestead, and that will contain about 10,000 workers and one mated, laying queen.

Visit the bees only on a sunny day. Wear white or any light-colored clothing. Never wear wool. Tuck your blouse or shirt into your pants and the pant legs into your socks.

Do not forget to wear a hat, gloves, and a bee veil. Don't wear perfume and make sure you are not reeking of farm/animal odors. Wash the beekeeping outfits regularly because any residual odor of past stings could trigger an attack alarm.

Use a smoker. Work barehanded only when you are already confident in removing your gloves. Smoke down the frames, then pry and lift a frame. Be careful and gentle with your movements, as any sudden, jerky actions will alarm the bees.

## Small-Scale Livestock

From the above list, urban and small-scale homesteaders can raise the following:

- Chickens
- Quails
- Ducks
- Rabbits
- Pygmy goats
- Dexter cattle
- Bees

Chickens are naturally quiet, and they are highly sought for their eggs and meat. Backyard varieties include the Cornish Cross, Freedom Ranger, and Red Ranger.

Ducks are great garden companions – this is if you're juggling tending livestock and growing vegetables. Small breeds are Rouens, Indian Runners, Blue Swedish, and Khaki Campbells.

Quails also have a small variety, the Coturnix. These can lay four-six eggs a week and will sell up to 50 cents per egg.

Champagne d'Argent, California, New Zealand, and Crème d'Argent can be bred and kept in a small area. When you plan accordingly, a small backyard could produce as many as a few hundred rabbits.

## Animals for Urban Homesteaders

In an urban setting, the pygmy goat can thrive because it is about half the size of a regular goat. The Nigerian Dwarfs can produce as much as one-two pints of milk. Their meat can still be harvested.

The Dexter cattle can be yours if you have at least half an acre of land. This land must have green grass where the animal could graze. Give it 18-24 months, and its 500-pound meat is ready for consumption. In the meantime, you can milk it for up to three gallons of fresh milk.

These same animals can be raised in community gardens, too. These are the spaces for people who want to homestead even when they live in the middle of the city. There are mobile slaughterhouses that can be commissioned when it is time for the animals to be harvested for meat.

Lastly, urban beekeepers can raise bees on their apartment rooftops.

Just remember to remain on the right side of the law when urban homesteading. If the local government allows livestock to be raised within the city limits, then that is great – just learn the regulations and requirements for all homesteading opportunities.

# How to Raise Backyard Chickens

With homesteading as your new passion, you are probably searching for ways to get those feet wet. Buying chickens is a great place to start your journey. These fowls are one of the sturdy foundations of homesteading, and this is because they can fulfill several goals.

What chickens traditionally offered factory farming has blurred. The non-negotiable life of self-sustenance, simplicity, and efficiency is now a life of options and convenience. Chickens can help you regain the more beautiful aspects of homesteading.

### Benefits of Raising Backyard Chickens

There are many other things that chickens can offer apart from eggs and meat. Of course, you cannot discredit the healthy option that free-range eggs provide. Store-bought eggs are not just bland; they barely provide the nutrients that your body needs.

Real chickens that roam freely act as chickens do, and they eat what chickens are supposed to eat. Layer feed is a wonderful supplement, but the chickens are meant to feed on proteins and greens.

Eggs produced by organic chickens contain more vitamins A and E. They also have omega-3 fatty acids and have lower fat and cholesterol.

A bird that is allowed to roam freely in its natural habitat also balances all the other elements on your homestead. Chickens can even help get rid of pests and parasites, plus they are also amazing gardeners as they love to nourish themselves with grub and the insects that feed on plants. Just make sure that they do not feed on the vegetables (warning, they like tomatoes).

And what about those mosquitoes that you worry about, as well as ticks and bugs? The risks of heartworm, malaria, and dengue virus are drastically cut down thanks to your feathered friends.

Chickens also naturally aerate the earth by pecking. This leaves a looser soil, so plants are better able to grow. They can aid in fertilizing the soil so you can look forward to greener gardens. Chicken manure can aid in increasing the potassium, nitrogen, and phosphorus contents of the soil.

To best use chicken manure, have it composted for about four to 12 months before you add it to your garden. You can speed up this process by rotating periodically so that the airflow is increased and the compost decomposes quicker.

Another benefit of raising chickens in your backyard is that you can harvest them for their meat. Free-range poultry tastes much different from factory farm chickens – and it does look different, too, with its smaller (yet tastier) breasts, chicken skin colors, and leaner meat. The store-bought chicken looks almost perfect because it was engineered to look that way – now doesn't that scare you?

There is also a sense of pride that comes with being able to provide for your family's needs. As soon as you understand the many benefits of setting the foundation of your homestead by nurturing chickens, then you will have an even higher appreciation for homesteading.

## The Meat Bird

Before you buy the chicks, first think of the purpose that they are going to serve. There are laying hens, and there are fighting cocks, but raising fast-growing fowls is a different arena.

With more chickens in your backyard, there is going to be more poop, so it's crucial to ask yourself now if you can handle this scenario. Also, are you okay with saying goodbye to the chickens every six-eight weeks? Would there be a problem with your kids turning them into pets and then not being able to let go when it is time to harvest the chicken meat?

To choose a meat bird variety, you could consider the Cornish Rocks that are a cross between the White Rock and Cornish. These can grow quickly with feed so you can harvest more meat as they increase in size.

You will likely purchase your meat birds as day-old chicks from the feed store or hatchery. Keep in mind that chicks require a lot of care. There should be a brooder area set up for them, with a heat lamp constantly keeping them warm. The brooder temperature also needs to be closely monitored.

Chickens can be kept in a coop (you'll learn about making one in a few minutes) with an attached small run. Have them run free, and you are raising happier chickens, so they are better able to produce omega-3s.

After the birds have grown to their full size (about five-seven pounds depending on whether they are roasters or broilers), it is time to harvest. You can slaughter the chickens right on your homestead or have them transported to the slaughterhouse and then processed.

Some farmers' markets buy birds, but you need to have the birds taken to a USDA-approved slaughterhouse or processing facility. There are mobile facilities in some states, so you can also opt for those.

## The Broody Hens and Eggs

If you are looking for laying hens so you can harvest eggs and eventually their meat, then you also need to learn how to pick the best breed, and how to house them and provide the supplies that they need.

You should raise free-range chickens, but if they need to be cooped and just be let out now and then because of the space limitations on your homestead, then that is fine, too.

Urban and suburban settings require fowl confinement, but even these birds need some fresh air and lots of sunshine, so you need to plan their living quarters, too.

Did you know that there are more than 200 chicken varieties nowadays? And you need to consider factors such as the climate, the breed temperament, egg-laying levels, and meat growing capabilities before you should set out to buy one.

If you are aiming for pure breed egg producers, then you can opt for Buff Orpingtons. Your other options include the:

- Leghorn
- Rhode Island Red
- Australorp
- Plymouth Rock
- Sussex
- Wyandotte
- Ameraucana
- Marans
- New Hampshire
- Silkie (this looks cute so be careful about turning them into pets)
- Brahma
- Cochin

- Welsummer

- ISA Brown

- Polish

- Jersey Giant

- Hamburg

- Minorca

- Barnevelder and the list could go on and on.

You can mix breeds if you are aiming for both meat and egg varieties. You will also need a rooster if you want to hatch chicks, but if you only want chickens for their eggs, then you do not need one.

Hens can produce eggs even without a rooster.

## Feeding the Chickens

As soon as you have bought the chickens, it is time to find out what you can do best to nourish them. The best diet for these birds will always be what Mother Nature provides for them – worms and insects, growing grass, clover, weeds, buckwheat, and seeds. If you have a rooster, you might also catch it feeding some mice to the hens.

Take note that they also need to eat some grit or coarse dirt because this helps them grind their foraged foods.

Backyard chickens can eat your kitchen scraps except for raw potatoes, beans, garlic, anything citrus, and onions. These scraps can make eggs taste different. Be sure to check on the things that your chickens are not supposed to eat, such as the pine shavings that are supposed to act as the litter and Styrofoam.

Hens that are raised on pasture produce deep orange egg yolks and have bouncy, viscous egg whites.

If you cannot pasture the chickens, then at least have a run attached to their coop so that they will not be depressed.

There are also supplements to the main feed, such as oyster shells (provides calcium), cabbage (more of an anti-boredom food for them), and commercial feed.

Just in case you run out of feed for the chickens, no worries – you can hard boil and then chop some eggs and have them eat them. Chickens can even go for a day or two without feeding, but make sure that they have ample drinking water.

If you are feeling up for a challenge, you can also make feed mix out of the seeds and grains that you grow in your backyard.

The feed types also depend on the age of the chickens that you are feeding. Chick starter is fed to chicks during their first six weeks. This should be about 22-24 percent protein if you are raising meat birds (broiler starter).

There are medicated and un-medicated varieties of chicken starter.

The grower pullet is fed from seven weeks up until 14 weeks. This has to be rationed because the laying chickens need to be given a diet with lower protein while the meat producers need to be fed 18 percent protein.

After this, the pullet developer (finisher) is fed at 14 weeks till about 22 weeks. The feed stores often sell a grower-finisher that has just the right amount of protein.

Laying hens at 22 weeks will soon require 16-18 percent of protein plus some calcium and minerals. They need all these for stronger eggshells. Layer feed needs are strictly fed when the bird is 22 weeks old because younger birds get damaged kidneys.

Roosters have been observed to eat laying rations.

As for the broiler rations, these are high-protein feeds meant for meat birds. The Cornish X Rock grows quite fast at 18-20 percent protein in their diet. The protein content for the grower-finisher feed may be lowered if the broiler is reaching its butchering age (about 12 weeks).

Heritage birds (chickens that can retain their historic characteristics) may be kept on a higher protein diet until they are slaughtered.

The only way to decrease the amount of commercial feed that you give to your chickens is to allow them to pasture because, then, they will eat enough weeds, bugs, grasses, and seeds.

## Building the Chicken Shelter

When the chicks have matured and are ready to move outdoors, you know that you already need a better shelter for them – but which one should you set up? Will it be a chicken coop, tractor, or henhouse? And here is another question that some homesteaders have already asked – can the doghouse or old shed be turned into a chicken coop?

The kind of coop that you build largely depends on how long the chickens are going to stay in that structure. Also, you need to plan whether you will construct a stationary and permanent structure or one that can be moved about.

Next, determine the amount of space that you are willing to set aside for your chickens. Never make the mistake of underestimating the measurements. You could begin small but might decide to expand the flock later.

Build a medium-sized coop as you test the waters.

If the backyard can provide ample foraging for your chickens, then you can construct two-three square feet of the coop for every bird. A bigger space is, of course, better because there will be more space for the chickens to roam around.

If you plan for the birds to be constantly cooped, or at least only during winter, then aim for about five to ten square feet for every chicken.

Chicken tractors can be moved around, and the right size for such is about five square feet for each chicken.

These are all general guidelines for backyard chickens. The bigger and more numerous the chickens are, the larger the space that you will need. Meat birds generally need bigger space than laying hens, just as full-grown pullets need a wider space than chicks.

Aggressiveness and pecking – should they ever become an issue – can be easily addressed by adding more space. Most of the time, these are just your chickens' way of saying that they are bored.

Chickens coops can be as simple as a wooden box with chicken wire. Save money by not going for the more elaborate designs. For urban and suburban folks, what you need is a secure coop that conforms to the building codes, homeowners association's requirements, zoning regulations, and other associations.

Laying hens typically need nest boxes. One box should be enough to accommodate four-five hens. Do not put in too many boxes because hens become broody (they constantly sit in the nest box) as they exert more effort to hatch the eggs.

Place the one-foot square boxes at two feet off the ground. Line them with shavings or straw, then attach them to the wall or place them on the shelves.

Laying chickens also need roosting space. The rule of thumb here is to provide six to ten inches of roosting space for every chicken. Again, the roosts must be two feet off the ground.

Check that the coop has ample shade, ventilation, and dust baths (dirt or dry soil). Place it on the eastern side of the homestead so that the chickens are warmed up during the morning but not burned in the afternoon.

### A basic DIY portable chicken coop plan

#### Materials:

- Lumber
- Metal braces
- Screwdriver and screws

- Sandpaper
- Carpenter's square
- Power miter
- Table saw
- Metal hardware cloth

## Method:

1. As soon as you have chosen the coop design, it is time to gather the 2'x 4' lumber for the bottom frame. Use metal braces for the corners and then screw the joints.

2. Make a perfect square with the bottom part of this frame. Use carpenter's square to check.

3. This movable coop will measure 9' x 8' or 72 square feet that is good enough for 24 chickens.

4. Rip the 2 x 4 lumber into thin pieces. These are going to be used for the diagonal rafters.

5. Using deck screws, assemble the pieces.

6. Traditionally, the space between the rafters is about 16", though 12"-14" can be good enough for smaller spaces.

7. Build the end frame using three vertical studs, forming a doorframe at both ends of the coop.

8. You can also attach two long stringers that will serve as the roost bars. Place a vertical bar to support the roost bars. Add these only when you are raising laying hens – no need for these when you are raising broilers.

9. You can also add nest boxes made of 2 x 2 boards secured with deck screws.

10. Place this box in the middle of the already constructed coop using deck screws.

11. Have a metal hardware cloth stapled at the bottom of the entire frame.

12. Add 4" to 6" of plywood and fasten with a deck screw.

13. Position the entire coop in your chosen location.

## Caring for Chickens in Winter

Here is rule number one – chickens do not need their own heaters during winter. Now that is established, here are some tips that can help you raise chickens even in the cold of winter:

## Deep Litter Method

This is a sustainable chicken manure management that many small homesteaders practice. It is a pile of compost (including your chickens' poop) in the middle of the coop flooring.

Just like any compost pile, start with a pine shavings layer, and then the chickens should take care of the poop. Add shavings, so the floor compost develops nicely. Don't worry about the aeration because the chickens will also take care of that for you.

The microbes in the litter should serve as probiotics (of sorts) for your hens.

Clean this annually or bi-annually, and you can then use the compost in your garden. For urban and suburban dwellers, you can simply clean the chicken litter weekly or monthly and then add it to your small compost bin.

## Use Supplemental Light

Great layers such as the Buff Orpington will still lay eggs during winter, but, generally, supplemental light is needed. A 40-watt light bulb that hangs at 7' off the ground should provide the right light intensity for your chickens to remain healthy. This is enough for a small chicken coop, the size of 100 square feet. For bigger coops (200 square feet or more), buy a 60-watt light bulb.

If you are willing to forego the winter eggs, then you can just respect the chickens' natural cycle and wait for them to be active again. Hens, after all, naturally rest during fall as they experience molting (losing their feathers), and their egg production decreases.

## Feed Them Corn

Feed the chickens some cracked corn in the evening so that they will stay warm. Corn is one of their favorite foods, so they will be happier as they rest with full tummies.

## Hang a Cabbage Head

You wouldn't want your chickens to be bored and depressed during winter, so you need to give them something to keep them busy. A simple cabbage head hanging on a string could be their toy. All the pecking should keep them busy all winter.

## Use Petroleum Jelly as Anti-Frostbite

During the coldest winters, you can keep the bigger breeds with huge combs and wattles safe from frostbite by applying petroleum jelly on those parts.

All in all, just let the chickens do what they want during winter. If they want to stay longer in the coop, then allow them. And they are a hardy bunch, so there is no need to shoo them indoors when it rains or snows.

## Predator Protection

### Potential chicken predators are:

- Dogs and cats (even your own pets)
- Hawks
- Foxes
- Weasels, minks, ermine
- Coyotes
- Raccoons
- Bobcats
- Snakes (they love chicks)
- Owls
- Fisher cats

- Rats

To keep the coop safe, you can dig a trench all around it (about 12 inches deep). Bury hardware cloth so that the digging predators cannot go in.

You can also elevate the coop so that rats, mice, and weasels will not get into it. Check the bottom of the chicken coop and be sure to patch holes. Turn on some form of lighting at night, or you can have motion sensor lights installed.

The compost pile must be kept at a good distance from the coop and make sure that feed leftovers are cleaned by nightfall. Use hawk netting for owl and hawk problems.

The last layer of protection for your livestock is a gun. Firing in the direction of the predator should be enough to deter its entry. Traps can also offend most predators, but be sure only to use these last two defenses if you have already tried the simpler ones.

# Your Homestead Pantry

So you have learned to grow and harvest your food. And now the fruits and vegetables – all colorful and beautiful – sit in baskets waiting for what needs to be done. Homesteading has, indeed, giving you fresh provisions that could potentially sustain your family.

Having year-round food security is the next step for your homesteading life, and you will need a homestead pantry to do that. Many people use pantries for smaller amounts of food, but as a homesteader, you could stock it up on months' worth of food (your goal is to build an annual stock for you and your family).

Do not force yourself to fill up huge shelves and freezers straight away – it takes time to transition from your current practice of grab-then-go to a life of stocking pantries.

To make things easy, you can divide pantry essentials into two groups: foods with a longer shelf life (e.g., rice, flours, and olive oil), and the perishables (e.g., meats, dairy, and fresh produce).

## The Essentials

### Flours

You can keep the all-purpose staple flour handy, but with the unhealthy gluten that you could get from it, perhaps, it is time to consider healthier options, such as whole grains, sourdough, and einkorn.

You only need to replenish flour every few months. Make sure also that they are stored in bins that are not directly exposed to sunlight. Check the flours every few weeks to make sure that they still smell fresh with zero traces of rancidity.

You can keep stocks of tapioca flours and whole-wheat flour, too.

## Fats and Oils

Exclusive of butter, you should store the essentials:

- Lard
- Avocado oil
- Olive oil
- Coconut oil

You can also include a bottle or two of extra virgin olive oil for those delicious salads and sauces that you'll soon make. This will also be a mouthwatering dip when paired with basil (pesto dressing).

## Sweeteners

It is time to cut down on your refined sugar consumption. Use natural sweeteners that will not give you the same sweet cravings as sugar does. There's maple syrup or honey that can be healthier alternatives. Organic cane sugar is also a healthier choice.

## Additional Items

- Homemade brown sugar
- Turbinado (raw) sugar
- Molasses

## Legumes, Dried Beans, Nuts, and Seeds

Every homestead pantry is not without dried beans. These can provide vitamin B, iron, minerals, selenium, potassium, calcium, and magnesium. They are also perfect ingredients for winter soups.

Keep stocks of seeds like split pea, lentils, and barley since these are also great for soup recipes. Other dried beans that you can harvest from your garden and include in your pantry are:

- Black beans
- Kidney beans
- Cranberry beans
- Pinto beans
- Popcorn
- Cannellini beans

Nuts can also be stored for as long as six months. So, go ahead and keep containers of salted almonds, walnuts, pecans, peanuts, and sunflower seeds.

## Canned Fruits and Vegetables

Your list of canned goods could change as the season changes. This depends largely on what crops you have harvested during the season. Canning, pickling, and other methods can preserve in-season vegetables, but be sure to do the process while the vegetables and fruits are still fresh and not when they are about to go bad.

As soon as you harvest these staples, make a habit of preserving them so you can ration your fruits and vegetables throughout the year:

- Tomatoes (this staple food preserves)
- Sauerkraut
- Green beans
- Beets
- Applesauce
- Peaches
- Cucumber
- Olives
- Corn

Spices and herbs can also be preserved when you add olive oil and then pour the mixture in ice trays.

## Dried Herbs

You can enjoy fresh herbs from your garden, but it would also be wise to store some by making dried herbs.

### Keep these herbs on hand:

- Thyme
- Bay leaves
- Oregano
- Tarragon
- Rosemary
- Herbs de Provence

### Vinegar

Just like olive oil, vinegar can help change the flavor of any dish. Vinegar is pretty easy to make. You can use leftover fruit juice, wine, or any alcoholic beverage. Here are a few recipes that you can use to make your own vinegar.

### For white vinegar –

### Ingredients:

Half a gallon of water

1-¾ cups of sugar

A packet of wine yeast or baking yeast

Balloon

Two cups of unfiltered vinegar

## Method:

1. Begin making the mother of vinegar by combining water and sugar. Heat them in a large pot, then keep stirring until the sugar has dissolved. Allow the sugar water to reach 110°F.

2. Pour the mixture into a glass jug then stir in the wine yeast.

3. Form an airlock by placing the balloon on the mouth of the jug. If the balloon becomes too big, make sure that you lift the neck to release some air.

4. As soon as the bubbles are gone (about two weeks), you can already pour the liquid into a stainless steel or huge glass container.

5. Put the unfiltered vinegar into the container and then cover it with layers of cheesecloth. Seal the neck using a rubber band.

6. Put the jug in a dark room at room temperature.

7. The mother of vinegar will form after a few days. This is that thin film over the vinegar surface.

To make other vinegar recipes, you can just replace the sugar water mixture with hard cider, leftover beers, white wine, red wine, or just about any alcoholic beverage.

### Salts

You could switch to sea salts for your organic recipes or use them to preserve your food harvests.

Keep these three salt types on hand:

● Himalayan sea salt

● Celtic sea salt

● Fleur de sel

The pink Himalayan sea salt is great for everyday seasoning, the Celtic sea salt has high mineral content, and the fleur de sel flakes are great toppings for bread.

# Declutter, then Organize

The rule here is simple - toss the things that you have not been using for more than six months (except your winter clothing and accessories) and then keep the ones that you use daily or weekly.

Next, put the dry goods into clear containers. You want to see where the sugar or flour is with one glance. Group the grains, beans, flours, sugars, and other pantry essentials. The bulk food items should be placed in the pantry, while smaller jars can be placed in the kitchen where they are readily accessible.

This basic homestead pantry can be expanded as you grow your homestead. Just take your time, plan, and soon you will save a lot of money as you reduce your grocery shopping trips. If you religiously preserve your harvests, then, eventually, you might even be able to feed off the land one hundred percent.

# PART THREE:
# HOMESTEADING SURVIVAL

# Extreme Weather Conditions on the Homestead

Do you know how some homesteaders are also doomsday preppers? They can't be blamed because the conditions on their homestead – the extreme weather conditions that can change in a snap of a finger – could easily make anyone feel fearful. But this need not be the scenario for you, too.

Earth's weather does bless (and sometimes curse) farms and many homesteads throughout the globe. Most of these conditions are manageable, but you can prepare for adverse weather.

## Drought

A drought is an event where there is a prolonged water shortage. With a family that would want to depend on homesteading, this is, indeed, bad news. There are many ways that you can prepare for drought, and these are broken down here according to your home, the garden, and your livestock.

*Your Home*

You can already use the rainwater barrel systems that you previously set up. Assuming that no laws are prohibiting you from setting up the rainwater collectors, then you can fill them up and store water.

Graywater (used, soapy water) can also be stored for toilet cleaning. Just make sure that you do not use harsh detergent.

*Your Garden*

You can also use the stored rainwater to water your plants. Mulching the garden will also benefit the plants, but stop fertilizing while the weather is not improving.

Pull the weeds so that the plants will not have nutrient competitors.

*The Livestock*

Make sure that all of the animals have a steady source of drinking water. Monitor them daily so you can take note of any that have grown weak. If there is a lactating cow or goat that is not currently able to provide milk to its calf or kid, then the offspring must be given supplements and feed.

Care must also be taken to keep animals from being trapped in dried up dams.

## Life-Threatening Heat

There is a phenomenon called the El Niño, which is periodic, large-scale warming that happens in certain areas of the planet. It can get extremely hot, so the effects of this event could affect you, your livestock, and the plants. Or there are moments when the summer season is just tremendously hot.

No one is immune from its effects, so it is best to protect yourself and every living creature on your homestead.

*Your Home*

Check your homestead pantry and see if you have ample stocks for your family's consumption. Make sure also that you have ample drinking water for everyone.

Dry, hot seasons aren't all bad, though. You can use the weather condition to dry fruits and vegetables, and even some herbs that you will store in your pantry.

*Your Garden*

Install a shade cloth over the garden beds where heat-sensitive crops (e.g., eggplants, tomatoes, peppers, and cucumbers) are planted. You can also plant these crops during the cool months so that you don't have to worry about losing them during the hot months.

See the drought tips on how to keep the soil moist.

Early on in your homesteading years, you can also make sure that you plant deciduous trees that can eventually cast a shade over your garden.

*The Livestock*

See the Drought section for livestock care tips.

# Snow

If there is too much heat, then your homestead could also potentially suffer from extreme cold. There are ways to protect your home and your garden during winter.

*Your Home*

Install insulators in your home so that you, your family, and pets can all snuggle safely indoors.

*Your Garden*

You can also install insulators in the greenhouse or heat it if the coldness goes way below the freezing point. Be sure to remove heavy snow from the hoop houses, greenhouse, and row covers.

Use row covers for the garden beds, and while the sun isn't showing, you can plant kale, leek, collard, cabbage, rutabaga, Brussels sprouts, turnips, parsnips, beets, and carrots.

Yet again, do heavy mulching so that the root crops will not freeze.

Winter is also the best time to organize the seeds and plan for poultry additions. You could even take this time to explore new plants and herbs that you could eventually plant.

*The Livestock*

You already learned how to take care of chickens during winter. As for the other animals, your goal while heavy snow is out there should be to keep them busy and happy.

Keep all animals well-fed, comfortable, and be sure to assist any pregnant animal. If you pasture most of your livestock, then they can be taken to the closed barn during winter. Just make sure that there is ample ventilation, food, and water.

The living areas also need to be cleaned regularly with the manure taken out. There should be enough space for the animals to walk around so that they can still exercise.

Meet every animal's nutritional requirements. Refer to the previous chapters for their feed and supplement needs.

# Wind

*Your Home*

Winds can come in different forms – like a hurricane, windstorm, tornadic winds, even gusts. To care for all your loved ones and even the structures on your homestead during windy seasons, be sure to stay indoors and go to the sturdiest shelter. If emergency managers are already telling everyone to evacuate, then leave – immediately.

*Your Garden*

The strongest gusty winds stress the plants during storm seasons.

Be wary of breaking branches and stems when the storms wreak havoc. Two combinations of weather could occur.

First, it can be extremely hot and windy. Even the slightest breezes can affect seedlings, so you need to protect your garden when these winds occur.

Second, it could get chilly and windy. The wind could heighten the effects of cold weather. Use a burlap windbreak during these wintry windy days. Support this setup with stakes. You can also create a wire mesh or ring for each plant and then fill it up with oak leaves or straw.

Don't forget to mulch so that the heat or cold effects are decreased.

*The Livestock*

If they cannot be evacuated, then the animals should be confined to the sturdiest shelter on your homestead. Go back to them the moment the situation clears.

## Lightning Storms

*Your Home*

Do keep in mind that it is never a good idea to go to the garden when a lightning storm is happening. Stay indoors at all times, and wait for the storm to stop. As soon as it is over, that's the only time that you should check on your garden, the chicken coops, and barn.

*Your Garden*

Keep all sensitive electronic gadgets away from the garden when there is a lightning storm forecast. The greenhouse controllers and irrigation timers should also be brought indoors.

The trees must also be trimmed so that they won't be damaged.

*The Livestock*

Install lightning protection systems at animal enclosures. Next, be sure to put fences all around the solitary, tall trees. You also need to lead all the animals away from water sources.

All animal shelters must also be built away from powerlines and trees.

# Living with Homestead Pets

Deciding to move to a homestead and alter your lifestyle is a huge step to make. By now, you know that it has benefitted your family in terms of health and perspectives; also, the new adversities that you experienced might even have strengthened you.

But have you ever wondered how your pets have also adjusted to this decision? If you already have dogs and cats before homesteading, then you need to get them to adjust to your new lifestyle. No more of those lazing-around-on-the-couch back in the city – it is time to welcome everyone to rural living.

It is all about ensuring that your pets still get the best environment even when they are already rural animals. Just as there are no pizza deliveries for your family, you will also have limited access to dog food, cat food, cat litter, and other furry pet needs, so adjustments have to be made.

You can choose to keep the pets indoors but think of all the advantages of training your dog to help you with your homesteading chores. Unsurprisingly, training your current dog to become a farm pet is just like getting a new farm dog and introducing it to farm life. Cats, though, are a different story.

## The Farm-Friendly Dog

Every homestead is unique, but there are common aspects, such as open space, gardening, chickens, other small animals, and predators.

Choose the dog that you will have on your homestead. Livestock guard dog breeds are:

- Central Asia Shepherd
- Akbash
- Maremma Sheepdog
- Anatolian Shepherd
- Armenian Gampr
- Polish Tatra
- The Great Pyrenees
- Kangal
- Tibetan Mastiff
- Russian Ovcharka, and
- Sarplaninac.

Have about eight well-bonded dogs form a pack. Their age could range from one and a half years to 13 and a half years. These dogs can help keep predators away from the homestead so you won't have to worry too much about foxes, stray dogs, eagles, hawks, and wolves. Certain farms even have mountain lions as predators, so be sure to have a pack of dogs ready to defend you.

Powerful, large dogs can also help pull the sled when you gather firewood and haul barrels of drinking water. They can ease your workload while providing personal protection.

Akbash and Great Pyrenees breeds are also great sources of fur. Their fur can be spun into yarn because they are as soft as baby alpaca fur.

Since these farm dogs are giving back the kindness that you are showering them, you should also make sure that they remain healthy at all times. Get in touch with a veterinarian for your dog's vaccinations. The five-way vaccine that counters kennel cough, hepatitis, parainfluenza, canine distemper, and parvovirus should be administered. You can include the anti-corona virus and leptospirosis if you opt for the seven-way vaccines.

Six-month-old puppies should already have their rabies vaccination.

As for their diet, you need to check the fat and protein content of their food. Growing pups need 22-25 percent protein, while adult dogs need only ten to 14 percent. Pregnant and nursing dogs need more protein (20-30 percent).

As for their fat needs, growing pups require just eight to 20 percent depending on their body mass. Adult dogs need five to 15 percent while pregnant, and nursing dogs require ten to 25 percent.

Carbohydrates are a great energy source for dogs, so you can include rice, oats, barley, and other grains in their diet. Do not feed them with human foods because this could lead to health issues and even early death.

If your farm animals can survive with kitchen scraps, well, your dogs must not. Add vitamin and mineral supplements, too.

### The Barn Cat

Again, you need to decide if you are going to keep a house cat or a barn cat. Here are some words of caution when it comes to cats in rural settings:

Never place city cats in a barn.

Never put kittens in a barn.

Kittens do not have the survival skills needed to evade horse hooves and such. Feral kittens, though, could survive.

Remember also that barn cats are more susceptible to parasites, rabies, feline leukemia, predators, and being hit by trucks. They can, however, help in controlling the rodent population, so there would be decreased grain losses and farm equipment damage.

An ideal barn cat is one that came with the farm, meaning it is a stray kitten that adapted to your family as you moved in. Just about any breed of a cat could live on a farm, but certain breeds could have advantages.

Shorthaired breeds will not let you worry about matted hair, hairballs, etc. Female cats are naturally better hunters compared to males, and the orange male variety is known to be the sweetest.

You need to confine a cat first if you want it to stay in your barn. Cage an old cat for about two-four weeks while new cats can be freed after a month. Include a litter box in the cage and feed it frequently so it will associate the cage with a safe zone.

Barn cats should still be fed even when they catch mice on your homestead. Feed them twice daily and provide ample fresh water. During winter, make sure that their water bowls are also heated. Schedule the second feeding at night and make sure that it is canned food so that the cats will stay indoors. As you do so, you keep them safe from predators like owls, coyotes, and raccoons.

Cats also need a lot of protein, so feed them with fresh fish and cooked meat.

Deworm the cats twice each year and make sure that they have a lofty station to rest on. You can also build their loft inside a sturdy shelter so that they have somewhere to go to when the weather isn't too friendly.

Just like dogs, barn cats also should be administered vaccinations. Combination vaccines for adult cats are the FVRCP that can counter feline distemper, feline leukemia, FeLV, calicivirus, and rhinotracheitis.

Treat your barn cats and farm dogs as members of your family by providing for their needs and loving them. They will even help you with some homesteading chores, so you should appreciate them more.

# Homesteading Alone

Most homesteaders take on the homesteading journey with a companion or their whole family. If you begin this journey alone, then you have more things to consider. It is not easy to homestead even when you are a pack, but taking on this lifestyle alone, equates to a lot of preparation. Failure to prepare could lead to sure disappointment.

The upside to homesteading alone includes having a sense of accomplishment. Imagine being able to grow and harvest everything that you need (on your own), protecting yourself, your plants, and livestock, and you are your own boss.

You will learn to be crafty when you are homesteading solo. You simply have to find ways to solve issues, and you can make things better without getting anyone's aid.

Sometimes, the scenario is that you still live with your family, but you run the homestead alone. This is okay, too.

Here are some basic projects that you can accomplish on your own:

- Build chicken coop
- Build other animal pens
- Make raised gardens
- Plant vegetables and fruits

- Build a fence all around the homestead
- Design and implement a compost pile system
- House maintenance

It is not impossible to do these even when you are alone, but you need to learn strategies that can help decrease the workload, avoid injuries, and take care of just the right number of animals.

# Game-Changing Decisions

### Reconsider the Number of Livestock

Homesteaders who love to take care of chickens happen to commit the same mistake – buy more of them. And before long, they see their farm teeming with chicks that are more than they can handle.

Or you might have taken up the egg production business, where you sell organic eggs, and before you know it, your success is eating up most of your time. Delivering 60 dozen eggs each month is a huge task for a lone homesteader.

Also, you need to feed the chickens, so the more that you keep, the more time it requires to feed them properly.

Chickens can forage for insects, nuts, and berries, but feeding them during the winter season can also be a challenge.

You will come to a point when you need to decide whether you will just harvest fruits, vegetables, and meats for your family's consumption. If you are literally alone, then see if you can just harvest for your needs.

You have to take care of yourself, too, so learn to cut down the chores and your livestock duties. Downsizing could give you that much-needed sanity, so take the time to consider it.

### Purchase the Right Equipment

It is also important to find, buy, and maintain the right equipment. You do not have to buy more because, for solo homesteaders, one set of equipment could address all needs.

Don't let equipment care eat your time. Buy quality equipment the first time so that you won't have to keep fixing it. Invest in a wheelbarrow, pull wagon, and basic gardening tools, like a hand trowel, garden scissors, weeder, pruning shears, curved blade shovel for digging, and flat digging shovel.

## Reassess Your Goals

Zero in on the goals that matter to you this year. List the things that bring you enjoyment, and be sure to include those as your goals. If keeping goats and fowls while tending to a garden already stresses you, then why do it?

Decrease the pressure on your workload, and you will surely lessen the stress on your body.

## Know the Downsides

Homesteading has many upsides, but there are also some downsides to it. To begin with, there are limitations to being a solo homesteader. Heavy lifting is almost impossible to do on your own. There are just a lot of homesteading duties that need more people.

Homesteading alone also brings just your skillsets. If your homestead suffers from an electrical problem because of a recent lightning storm and you have zero knowledge about electricity, then you will pay a professional to do it. This is also the case with repairs on machinery and equipment.

While the joys of homesteading include being proud of your solo accomplishments, the downside to this is that you also have no one to share your problems with. And homesteading can be overwhelming so it could get lonely.

Sustaining injuries or getting ill could also be glaring disadvantages to homesteading on your own. While you can call 911 and wait for a response, what about for situations that require, say, CPR?

## Battling Loneliness

Face it – homesteading alone can get flat-out sad. The isolation will not make quick trips possible, so you are alone in the middle of nowhere.

Homesteading solo will result in more alone time. You might feel then that the walls are caving in and that your decision to homestead might be a mistake.

Many homesteaders have admitted their struggles with rural melancholy, but some fight it with chores on the farm. As you previously learned, you could be an introvert or extrovert, so, at times, it is all a matter of personality.

Introverts might survive longer in isolation, but extroverts need to divert their thoughts to other things. If you feel that socialization should be a part of your day-to-day existence, then do not sign up immediately to a solo homesteading life.

Think twice before changing your lifestyle.

Now, if you have already made the decision and you need to cope with slower days, then here are some simple tips:

## Start a Blog

One bored person + Lots of Time + the Internet = Probable Passion

You can begin an online business to keep busy or write a blog. Dig deep within you and find out what really excites you. If you want to blog about your decision to homestead solo, then go ahead and write about that. With homesteading becoming more and more popular each year, all it takes is consistency in writing, and you could become an Internet sensation.

## Think That It's a Transition Period

The first part of homesteading is always the hardest – every homesteader can attest to this. If you look at the first few months as an adjustment phase, then you can prepare and plan for the upcoming months.

There is so much to do on your homestead, so do those things. As you get used to doing them, then you will soon have a renewed passion for homesteading.

## Socialize

Use the Internet to seek out your old high school friends on Facebook. Email those that do not have Instagram or Facebook. You don't need physically to be in front of a person to socialize.

Nowadays, a single click of a button means you can get in touch with your relatives or friends.

Homesteading alone need not be lonely. It is up to you to make it more exciting and fruitful (literally and figuratively!).

# Money-Saving Crafts and DIY Projects

You have just learned about how homesteading can get quite lonely, at first, as well as how to counter melancholy on your homestead. Another way to counter rural loneliness – and an effective one at that – is to make some DIY crafts.

Instead of spending a hefty amount on furniture and appliances, how about you craft your own? If this is too big a project for now, then try these simple DIY crafts:

### DIY Aqua Dam

If you set up your homestead in a flood-prone area, then you need to make sure that your family will be protected from the onslaught of rains. Building an aqua dam should solve this problem for you.

An aqua dam is a barrier filled with water that can help divert waters. All you need are some inner tubes, fill them with water, and then create a temporary barrier.

### Organic Weed Killers

Support and protect the garden from invasive species. The easiest solution is to use vinegar at its full strength. Pour apple cider vinegar into a sprayer and spray directly on the affected areas. A word of caution – it could also kill good plants, so spray only when you are sure that it is the weed that you're killing.

This is a pet and livestock safe weeder, so spray away. If you are still worried, then you may reduce its acidity by five percent. Just add a little water.

## Other Options

### Vinegar and dishwashing soap mixture

Use an ounce of dishwashing soap with every gallon of pure vinegar. This can also be used as a garden insecticide. If you do not want to harm the plants, then use organic dishwashing soap as well.

### Vinegar + soap + salt

Use a gallon of vinegar to every cup of salt and one tablespoon of dishwashing liquid. Mix the ingredients then apply to the affected areas.

### Vinegar + lemon juice

Many homesteaders can attest that mixing lemon juice with vinegar can heighten its weed-killing properties. Add a cup of lemon to a gallon of vinegar.

### Vinegar + essential oil

Mix pure vinegar with a tablespoon of orange or clove essential oil. The oil is believed to stick to the garden plants, thus, increasing the mixture's effectiveness.

# DIY Backyard Incinerator

Also known as a burn barrel, this is a 55-gallon metal drum with an open head. You can modify this to burn household trash cleanly and safely.

## Materials:

- Steel drum
- Drill or handgun to make the air holes

- Two concrete blocks
- Heavy fencing or metal grate (to cover the mouth of the barrel)
- Sheet metal (as barrel cover)

## Method:

1. First, pick a location for your burn barrel. This should be away from trees and not where it could encounter prevailing winds. Situate it away from any combustible material.

2. Drill air holes into the metal drum; about 20 on different sides and at different heights.

3. Drill four more holes, measuring about half an inch each. These should be drilled at the bottom of the metal drum so that rainwater can drain.

4. Use a fire cover (grill top) and bend it so it can loosely fit.

5. The steel siding can serve as the rain cover for the burn barrel.

6. As soon as the holes are drilled, set up the barrel on two concrete blocks. The edges of your drum barrel should be placed on the blocks, but air space must also be left. This allows air to flow freely and helps with the drainage.

7. Cover the barrel when it is not in use so that the contents will not get wet.

# DIY Citrus All-Purpose Cleaner

Many people admit that they are tired of paying big bucks for chemical cleaners that require a gas mask to use safely. The thing is, homemade versions are just as good – if not better.

If you have been using a 50-50 mixture of vinegar and water for the longest time and you want to stir things up a bit, then you can try this citrus cleaner for a change.

This citrus cleaner is still an organic mixture that you can use without worry. It is even a wonderful way to use the citrus peels that the goats and chickens don't pay attention to.

## Ingredients:

- One to two quart-sized mason jars

- Spray bottle

- Strainer

- Lime, orange, lemon, or grapefruit peels (two or more of these would also work)

- Three-four drops of grapefruit, lemon, or orange essential oils (optional)

- Water

## Method:

1. Fill the jars up halfway with citrus peels. Pack the jars if you want to. You can also combine grapefruit, lemon, and orange peels.

2. Fill the rest of the jar with white vinegar. Cover then give it a good shake.

3. Steep the vinegar and peel mixture for two-three weeks. The longer that you leave it, the more potent it will become.

4. After the required steeping period, take out the peels and strain using a fine strainer. This should remove the citrus bits that are left floating in the mixture.

5. Dilute with water (one part mixture with one part water) then pour it into a spray bottle.

6. Add three-four drops of citrus essential oils to boost the scent further.

You can use this natural cleaner on the floors, bathtub, kitchen sink, countertops, and toilets. Have fun cleaning because you don't have to suffer from the chemical odors any longer.

## DIY Paper

Making basic paper is easy and fast, but it can take several days before it dries completely.

## Method:

1. Use a food processor or blender to shred the ingredients. You can use newspaper (this is the most economical) to start. Add just enough water so that the paper becomes damp but not wet. Add a glob of white glue as well.

2. Spread the blob on the fine screen. Flatten and smoothen the paper.

3. Put it in a dry area, then wait for the paper to dry. Never place in direct sunlight, though. If mold starts to grow, then you need to throw it out and restart.

Homemade paper can be used as gift tags, Origami material, and journal sheets.

# DIY Candles

Do you like the sweet scent of beeswax candles? Homemade candles are much safer for you because they do not release toxic matter into the air. There are three ways that you can make homemade candles:

### Candle Dipping

Hold the hot wax in one container and cold water in a second container. Take turns in dipping into the hot wax, then into the cold water, and into the hot wax again.

You can make two candles at a time when you use both ends of a wicked string. Hang the candles to dry for a couple of days.

### Candle Molding

You can also get creative and craft the shapes that you want. You could start with the basic empty milk carton. Place ice cubes around wicks then pour in the hot wax.

Allow the mold to cool before removing the carton. You will see that the candle will have beautiful, decorative holes.

## Rolled Candle

Another fun way to make candles is to roll a wax sheet around the center wick. Make beeswax or buy it to create a honeycomb mold.

Lay the wick along the edge then roll it up. Warm the beeswax sheet first in your hands so that it won't crack.

Here is a little safety advice - never leave burning candles unattended. Be sure to create and discuss a fire safety plan in your home. Install fire extinguishers, smoke detectors, and other fire deterrents.

# DIY Detergent

Homemade soaps and laundry detergents are catching a lot of attention lately because of their potential money-saving aspects. This solution that you are going to learn now can clean even the toughest stains (e.g., stained cloth diapers). Compared to commercial detergents, it is even better because it does not contain phosphates and sodium lauryl sulfate.

### Ingredients/Tools:

- One bar of soap (about $3.25)
- Half a box of borax ($3.97 per 72-oz. box)
- One cup of washing soda - not baking soda! ($8.49 per 55-oz. box)
- Several cups of water
- Essential oils (different price for every scent)
- Five-gallon bucket
- Water
- Cheese grater
- Medium saucepan

### Method:

1. Using a cheese grater, coarsely grate the soap.

2. Put the shreds into a medium saucepan filled with a few cups of water.

3. Heat then stir until all the soap pieces dissolve.

4. Add borax and the washing soda. Stir and dissolve the recently added ingredients.

5. Pour the mixture into the five-gallon bucket. Fill it three-quarters of the way with hot water. Stir thoroughly, then leave it to sit, undisturbed, throughout the night.

The homemade detergent will look like a gel chunk, and its yield will be about three-four gallons depending on the amount of water that you added. You can leave the block of detergent in the bucket or use smaller jugs or buckets to store the smaller portions.

You can dispense using a drink dispenser, or you can just scoop it out of the bucket when you finally need it.

# DIY Curtains

Learning how to make your own curtains can give you the freedom to make shapes and designs that you want. Isn't it just frustrating if you find the right color, patterns, and texture on a curtain only to be told that it does not come in your window size?

Homemade curtains are also better for people with allergies because now you can choose the materials to use. Find curtain materials that are easily washable every couple of months. This is crucial for people who suffer from dust mite allergy.

You will need basic sewing skills to do this project. If you are good with those, then read on:

### Method:

1. Measure the windows that you want to cover. Remember to measure beyond the window frames.

2. Create dimensions for every layer. Add seam allowances of about 5/8 (standard).

3. Decide how each of the curtains will be attached to the rod. The hanging distance will shorten with the depth that will wrap around the rod, so be sure to include that in your calculations.

4. Measure the amount of fabric that you need for this project.

5. Draw the patterns on a big piece of tissue paper. As long as your design is symmetrical, you can fold the fabric as you cut along its edge.

6. Continue with the sewing pattern. Pin the paper, cut, and then sew.

## DIY Baskets

Baskets have many uses on a homestead. Imagine carrying the basket around and filling it with freshly harvested fruits and vegetables. There are various basket-weaving techniques that you can employ.

You can make wisteria baskets or be more creative with the bark basket. Poplar trees undergo a growth phase from April until June. In this phase, the bark can be easily cut and peeled off.

You can use these peeled barks as the sides of your basket. Don't expect the basket to form a flat bottom because it won't, but you can create a strap for it.

Using a crisscross pattern, use hickory soaked in water as the lace. Punch holes on the sides of the bark, then lace them up.

The size of the basket will depend on the size of the bark that you cut.

## DIY Paint

The egg tempera paint has been around for many centuries. Medieval paintings used a lot of this type of paint. Oil paint may also be formulated using linseed oil and milk paint with casein (dried milk protein).

Pigment (use natural materials like herbs, rust, and mud)

Binder (holds the pigment onto the painted surface)

Solvent (used to thin out paint)

## Method:

If you want to make egg tempera paint, you can use watercolor tube paints, egg yolk as a binder, some water, and solvent (optional).

For the casein paint, use skim milk made sour with lemon juice. Leave overnight, then strain the curds and add the pigments. Don't worry about the odor because it will quickly fade as the paint dries.

Painting does not have to leave toxic fumes, and now you can keep busy when you do small painting projects.

Now, you can say bye-bye to boredom!

# 14 Homesteading Income Ideas

The DIY crafts that you just learned are potential cash cows. So, yes, you can sell the detergent, all-purpose citrus cleaner, curtains, and even the candles that you crafted. There are many online sellers of these crafts and organic cleaners, so you might want to follow their footsteps by creating a website for your unique products. However, since you said sayonara to a life of convenience to live a healthier (and potentially happier) life, you can look deeper into your goals.

Being a homesteader means you want a life outside of the easy life that you were/are currently living. So get back to that target and decide what you can get out of homesteading.

## Sell Homegrown Products

Before you tackle this head-on, check the food safety laws in your area first. Once you have those covered, especially when you are going to sell milk or meat, then you can go ahead and sell your organic produce.

1. If you don't want to deal with the red tape, then the workaround is to sell the animals instead of their food products. This means you can sell the live chicken and not just its meat.

2. You can also sell chicken eggs or eggs from geese or ducks. One dozen chicken eggs could sell for $4 or more, so imagine if you can

sell 70 dozen each month (and this is still a small-scale egg business) –
you get $280.

Everybody seems to want organic eggs nowadays. People prefer it
for its omega-3 fatty acids that are good for your eyes, heart, and skin.

3. You can also sell gallons of fresh milk. The extra milk that your
family can no longer consume may be sold in farmers' markets. You
can also begin a goat-share or cow-share program if you don't want to
worry about those laws.

A cow-share or herd-share agreement is much like owning stocks
in a company. A consumer will pay a farmer for caring for his or her
goat or cow and eventually for milking the animal. The owner of the
herd-share will obtain the milk from his or her own animal.

4. Selling homemade dairy products, such as cheese and butter,
can also be a source of income for you and your family.

5. You can also sell broiler meats and other fowl meats. For bigger
sales, you can sell pork and beef.

6. How about selling heritage ducks, geese, or turkeys? Livestock
conservation has also been causing quite a stir lately. Rare breeds of
poultry and livestock are now being conserved and sold as heritage
animals.

Consider the long-term plan for conservation breeding. What
species would you raise – are they going to be large or small animals?
Will you deal with fur or feathers?

Just as you would care for regular livestock, you need to learn
about animal husbandry, feeding, and other animal needs. More
importantly, you can add learning about the characteristics of the
species that you will sell as a heritage animal.

7. How about fertile eggs? If you've got a rooster in the flock, then
you can sell fertilized eggs online. See if you can have the fertile eggs
shipped, but before you do, check the fertilization rates. Provide a
rough estimate for the hatchlings because even the healthiest clutches
seldom hatch out.

8. Have you heard of stud services? If you have ample space to keep the male animals, then you can rent out their service. This could make you some good money, especially when you have rare animal breeds on your homestead.

Keep tabs on the fertility of the roosters, the buck, and the male cattle. Even your farm dogs can be rented out for their stud services. If you get more clients from this business, then you might like to set up a stud farm.

You need to design a program that mitigates diseases and pathogens. Take time to set up a meeting with stud managers. You are the boss' boss, so you get to decide what is best for them; however, be sure to quarantine the ladies at some point and separate the pens of every male animal.

Register the sires, and you will bring in even more money. You might also consider semen collection done by certified or registered semen collectors.

9. Fiber animals can also provide income opportunities if extra activities such as shearing fleece are okay for you. The fleece that is harvested needs to be skirted and cleaned before you can market it. There is also a market for unwashed fleece.

Clean fibers are sold by the pound, and these can also be made into roving. If you have spinning skills, then you can spin a yarn of varying thicknesses and weights.

10. Selling honey can also provide a sizeable input into your homestead income. It's time to put your honey harvesting skills to good use. Harvest the raw honey, filter it, and then bottle it. The bees can take care of the honey-making process for you while you search for people who have a constant requirement for your product.

Probable honey clients are bakers, chefs, and those who make organic soaps, shampoos, and body washes.

11. Apart from the livestock sales, you can also sell plant products such as heirloom seeds (it has the same concept as the heirloom livestock) and transplants.

Transplants are extra plants that can be sold for ornamental or conservation purposes. Selling edibles such as berries, mushrooms, and fruits is also a great way to make extra money from your homestead.

12. Another profit booster is growing trees. Some homesteaders do not want to go through buying the seeds, planting them, and then growing the process of the tree.

As a tree grower, you would need fruit seeds to jump-start your business. The most profitable fruit trees that homesteaders search for are:

- Avocado – sells for $10/7" plant; sells at $30 for every 8" plant
- Mandarin – $5 per 7" plant; can be sold for $25 for the 8" plant
- Lemon – $5; $15
- Persimmons – $10; $35
- Orange – $5; $25
- Pomegranate – sells for $10 for every 7" plant; $35 for each 8" plant

*Here's an easy tree-planting schedule*

- One month – plant the fruit seeds inside pop cans.
- Two months – replant the one-two cm seedlings into plastic cups.
- Three months – replant the small plants into individual two-liter plastic bottles.

Since you grow the fruits yourself, you can go ahead and label the seeds as organic. If you can wait until the plant reaches two feet, then you can earn twice as much. Graft a branch from the same kind of tree. This should cause the tree to produce fruits.

You can grow seeds from any windowsill in your home. It is better to grow them inside because they can be exposed to torrential rains and snow. They could even be blown over by gusty winds, so have them grow in the safety of your home for now.

13. Make and Sell Furniture

One of the businesses that you can link with your homesteading life is crafting handmade furniture and selling your wooden arts. If you are truly serious about adding this to your load, here are the things that you need to do:

1) Find a niche that will suit your carpentry skills. There are home furnishings, office furnishings, custom-built pieces, and built-in cabinetry. You can sell your furniture online or have a small brick-and-mortar store within your homestead. You can even target a smaller niche, such as installing upholstery.

2) Location is everything, so your furniture-buying customers will surely be amazed to find your shop on a rural farm.

3) Obtain the relevant permits and licenses.

4) Write your business plan.

5) Don't forget to find inspiration for your furniture designs.

6) Lastly, create a handmade furniture website.

You can make furniture from different materials. You could learn woodworking skills or use metals or glass to create home accents.

14. Consulting Business

Once you become great at your homesteading life, you can even begin a consulting business. As a consultant, you can advise on how to start homesteading, what livestock would go best in what size and type of land, and what fruits and vegetables to grow. People can also ask for your expertise when they want to sell products from their homestead and when they want to expand.

Today, you are just learning about these basic homesteading principles and skills, but someday you can be so much more.

# Conclusion

Homesteading is a rewarding life - no doubt about that -, but to be able to enjoy the benefits, there are certain terms to define, qualities about you that you need to discover, and skills that you need to learn.

Homesteading is also control over your health, food, home, and your life in general. And just as you would with any project, it also needs commitment, planning, a serious self-assessment, and preparation for the challenges ahead.

Many tests could come with homesteading, but the one that you need to overcome more than anything is rural loneliness. Besides this, you should also steer clear of the most common homesteader mistakes by being armed with information, designing a plan, setting the correct budget, proper land inspection, just to name a few.

Being a homesteader also means acquiring specific skills, such as composting, gardening, salvaging, food preservation and storage, milling, animal husbandry, cooking, and even the basic skill of starting a fire. And as the leader of your pack, you should also protect livestock from predators and other possible sources of harm.

Then there are the costs of the land and other homesteading equipment, machinery, and materials that should be calculated before you even make the initial offer, which is why you need to be up-to-date on the local homesteading laws and regulations. Doing so will be the only way to conduct your business without any worries.

As these things are settled, you can focus on raising your livestock and growing your produce from your garden (that you can grow better with some useful hacks). And while you are at it, you can learn some DIY crafts that can treat your boredom and even add to your income.

The beautiful end goal of homesteading is to live off the land one hundred percent. To do this, systems should be established, and you will then be able to recognize all the income-generating opportunities on your homestead.

Congratulations! You are now a well-informed homesteader.

# References

(n.d.). Retrieved from
https://www.youtube.com/watch?v=YJewpW3lpzc

(n.d.). Retrieved from
https://youtube.com/watch?v=jO19XxEXmmQ&list=PLg8oaaTdoHz
MxpqfzRHzxC-qf9Ej60dBK&index=1

(n.d.). Retrieved from
https://www.youtube.com/watch?v=YvOW56x29B0

12 things to know about raising cows | Hello Homestead. (n.d.).
Retrieved from https://hellohomestead.com/12-things-to-know-about-
raising-cows/

Annie. (2018, June 13). Tips For Having A Large Homestead.
Retrieved from https://15acrehomestead.com/large-homestead/

Annie, Cook, J., Stone, K., & Abernathy, W. T. (2019, March 31).
The Ultimate Guide To Garden Soil. Retrieved from
https://15acrehomestead.com/ultimate-guide-garden-soil/

Arcuri, L. (2019, May 24). What Is Homesteading? Retrieved from
https://www.thespruce.com/definition-of-homesteading-3016761

Arcuri, L. (2019, December 12). How to Survive as a Beginning
Homesteader. Retrieved from https://www.thespruce.com/top-tips-for-
the-beginning-homesteader-3016686

Basket Making. (n.d.). Retrieved from https://www.sage-urban-homesteading.com/basket-making.html

Caitlin, Emma, Evelyn, Gibbs, L., Stephanie, Patti, ... Maria. (2020, January 9). Great Benefits of Homesteading. Retrieved from https://theelliotthomestead.com/2014/01/great-benefits-of-homesteading/

Cory, D. (2019, July 26). A Beginner's Guide to Small-Scale Homesteading. Retrieved from https://dengarden.com/gardening/Small-Town-Homesteading

Davidson, M., Davidson, M., & Alexa Weeks. (2019, December 12). 10 Most Important Homesteading Skills. Retrieved from https://homesteadsurvivalsite.com/important-homesteading-skills/

Dodrill, T. (2019, December 10). How to Find the Perfect Piece of Land for Your Homestead. Retrieved from https://homesteadsurvivalsite.com/how-to-find-land-homestead/

Garman, J., Tony, Brenda, Lana, Ana, Robin, ... Homesetading Skills. (2018, February 1). 6 Homesteading Skills to Learn First. Retrieved from https://timbercreekfarmer.com/6-homesteading-skills-to-learn-first/

Home. (n.d.). Retrieved from https://homesteadlady.com/

Homemade Candles and Candle Making. (n.d.). Retrieved from https://www.sage-urban-homesteading.com/homemade-candles.html

Homemade Paint Formula. (n.d.). Retrieved from https://www.sage-urban-homesteading.com/homemade-paint.html

Homemade Paper Making. (n.d.). Retrieved from https://www.sage-urban-homesteading.com/homemade-paper.html

Homesteading – Advantages of Self-Sufficiency on Your Own Property. (n.d.). Retrieved from http://environmentalprofessionalsnetwork.com/homesteading-advantages-of-self-sufficiency-on-your-own-property/

How Many lands You Need for a Homestead or Farm. (2018, April 13). Retrieved from https://highsierrapermaculture.com/2018/02/20/how-much-land-homestead/

Ikona, A., D., B., Brenna, Martinelli, M., Martinelli, M., Brown, M., & Marvin. (2019, October 23). Growing Trees For Profit In Your Backyard: Homesteading. Retrieved from https://homesteading.com/growing-trees-profit-backyard/

Johm, Val, Julie, Stacy, Toni, Kathryn, ... Ruth. (2018, January 30). Bringing a Barn Cat (or two) to Your Homestead. Retrieved from https://104homestead.com/barn-cat-homestead/

Kristyn, Kim, H, A., Jill, Krystyn, Amanda, ... Lorenzen, E. (2018, September 19). DIY Pallet Garden; How to make Raised Wood Pallet Garden Bed. Retrieved from https://busycreatingmemories.com/diy-pallet-garden/

Lynn, Lynn, Katie, Katie, Stacey, Stacey, ... Simple Living Country, Gal. (2019, October 6). 7 Steps to take before you begin your homesteading journey. Retrieved from https://simplelivingcountrygal.com/7-steps-to-take-before-you-begin-your-homesteading-journey/

Marie, Linda, Amanda, & L, T. (2019, November 4). What's the Big Deal GMOs? Retrieved from https://rurallivingtoday.com/homesteading-today/big-deal-gmos/

McCleod, B. R. (2015). Neo-Homesteading in the Adirondack North Country: Crafting a Durable Landscape. Neo-Homesteading in the Adirondack North Country: Crafting a Durable Landscape, 2. Retrieved from https://etd.ohiolink.edu/!etd.send_file?accession=antioch1440152751&disposition=inline

Ogden Publications, Inc. (n.d.). Guide to Urban Homesteading. Retrieved from https://www.motherearthnews.com/homesteading-and-livestock/self-reliance/guide-to-urban-homesteading-zm0z14amzrob

Ogden Publications, Inc. (n.d.). A Guide to Buying Homestead Land. Retrieved from https://www.motherearthnews.com/homesteading-and-livestock/guide-to-buying-homestead-land-zmaz82ndzgoe

Pantry Essentials: Ingredients For a Well-Stocked Homestead Kitchen. (2018, December 7). Retrieved from https://thechildshomestead.com/cooking/pantry-essentials/

Patterson, S. (2014, December 22). 3 Priceless Benefits Of Modern Homesteading. Retrieved from https://www.offthegridnews.com/how-to-2/3-priceless-benefits-of-modern-homesteading/

Pawning Through the Ages. (n.d.). Retrieved from https://www.history.com/shows/pawn-stars/articles/pawning-through-the-ages

Poindexter, J., & PoindexterJennifer, J. (2018, April 21). Raising Sheep: A Complete Guide on How to Raise Sheep at Homestead. Retrieved from https://morningchores.com/raising-sheep/

Queck-Matzie, T. (2019, March 13). Farming 101: How to Plant Corn. Retrieved from https://www.agriculture.com/crops/corn/farming-101-how-to-plant-corn

sadie423. (2019, August 13). How to Raise and Care for Goats. Retrieved from https://pethelpful.com/farm-pets/how-to-care-for-goats

Staff, M. C., & MorningChores StaffMorningChores Staff is a team of writers and editors who collaborate to create articles. If the article you are reading is authored by MorningChores Staff. (2019, August 20). 12 Things You Need to Know Before Getting Your First Ducks. Retrieved from https://morningchores.com/about-raising-ducks/

Suwak, M. (2019, October 3). 11 Fast Growing Vegetables For Your Homestead. Retrieved from https://www.primalsurvivor.net/fast-growing-vegetables/

The Editors of Encyclopaedia Britannica. (2014, May 21). Animal husbandry. Retrieved from https://www.britannica.com/science/animal-husbandry

The Ultimate Guide to Farm Dogs on the Homestead from Homestead.org. (2019, January 9). Retrieved from https://www.homestead.org/homesteading-pets/the-ultimate-guide-to-farm-friendly-dogs/

Thoma, M. (2019, September 30). How to Prepare Your Garden For Extreme Weather Conditions [37 Tips!]. Retrieved from https://tranquilurbanhomestead.com/extreme-weather/

Tipsbulletin. (2019, December 14). 70 Wonderful Uses of White Vinegar. Retrieved from https://www.tipsbulletin.com/vinegar/

Vicky, Bedford, L., Hartmann, L., & Marti. (2019, October 28). These 70 Gardening and Homesteading Hacks Will Blow You Away • New Life On A Homestead: Homesteading Blog. Retrieved from https://www.newlifeonahomestead.com/70-gardening-homesteading-hacks-will-blow-away/

Weeks, A. (2019, December 13). 12 Fun DIY Projects For Homesteaders. Retrieved from https://homesteadsurvivalsite.com/diy-projects-for-homesteaders/

Winger, J., Nichole, Nichole, Jill, Jill, Stacie, ... Christian Homefront. (2018, March 18). How to be an Apartment Homesteader • The Prairie Homestead. Retrieved from https://www.theprairiehomestead.com/2011/10/how-to-be-an-apartment-homesteader.html

Printed in the USA
CPSIA information can be obtained
at www.ICGtesting.com
LVHW020255080923
757611LV00002B/4